# The
# Homeschool
# EXPERIMENT
## ~ A Novel ~

# Charity Hawkins

## Familyman ministries
www.familymanweb.com

This book is dedicated to my husband,
who encourages my dreams,
cherishes our family,
and sacrifices for us all.

And to the Lord,
because unless He builds this house,
we labor in vain.

# Contents

# Acknowledgements

Thank you God, for doing exceedingly, abundantly, beyond all I asked or imagined. Thank you for carrying me along.

Thank you, my wonderful husband, for watching the kids an inordinate amount of time, for putting away the dishes without being asked, for encouraging my dreams, and listening to my heart. You are my Prince, always. I love you.

To my sweet children, thank you for bringing joy, giggles, hugs, and gifts to my everydays. You are my darlings and my dears and the lights of my life and the treasures of my heart. I love you forever.

To my parents, thank you for helping me realize that any bizarre idea might be completely feasible. And Mom, thank you for your detailed and thoughtful editorial advice. Tammy, thanks for staying up late to read, encouraging the idea of a book, and being a great sister.

To my parents-in-law, who are nothing like the parents-in-law in the book, thank you for being incredibly supportive of us, not only in words, but in taking our children to the pizza place more than could be reasonably expected of any person. Thank you for giving me a much-needed break on a regular basis; I couldn't do this without you.

Thank you, my dear friends and mom editors: Megan (the first), Amy, Lorraine, Liz, and Kendra. Thank you Julie, Katie, Erica, Dana, Amber, Jessica, Lisa, Leslie, Carrie, Amy T., Kelly, April, Jenni, and Melissa. Thank you for your honest and essential feedback, and for your enthusiastic encouragement. You are kindred spirits.

To the Titus 2 women who loved me so much they shared with me not only the gospel of God, but their lives as well, thank you for collectively being my "Lisa." Thank you Leah, Liz, Leslie, and Ronna.

And, to Todd and Debbie, thank you for taking a chance.

# Foreword

I'm not sure what it is about being an author, but as soon as you've written a book or two people start to think that you know some secret formula of how to get a book into the hands of readers. In fact, I've been cornered dozens of times to hear about *a great book idea* and have been handed manuscripts in various forms *to see what I think*.

Usually, I get to around the third paragraph on the first page and know that this book "doesn't fit our…um…er…distinct criteria" of encouraging parents in what's most important.

From our first contact, Charity Hawkins (that's her pen name), distinguished herself from the crowd. Maybe it was her sincerity to partner with us, her well-thought-through idea that she presented us with, or the chocolate she included for our reading enjoyment that set her apart, but we decided to look through her manuscript. I must admit that in the back of my mind I was thinking, *That's the end of that…even though she is sincere.*

At the time we were up to our eyeballs in our speaking tour, zigzagging across the country in our big RV filled with all eight of our children. Behind the wheel, I was certainly in no position to look over a manuscript, but one day as we were tooling down the highway I looked over at my wife, who was riding shot gun, and saw her open a large, three-ring binder.

"What are you doing?" I asked.

She told me she was going to start reading Charity's manuscript. *That won't last long*, I thought. For a little while my wife read in silence and then… she laughed…outloud.

I was shocked because my wife is a tough customer and doesn't laugh easily when she reads. A thought crept into my head — perhaps this book is different. I'm not sure if I said anything at that moment but after her second laughter outburst, I asked her what was so funny.

She relayed a couple of humorous stories, but what my wife was most struck by was the realness with which the author wrote (something we hold as a premium). There was no pretense, expert advice, or lofty goals…just a fellow mom who experiences firsthand, the hard, hilarious, and rewarding life of trying to homeschool her children.

As my wife talked, I could tell she was hooked. In fact, over the next few days, each time she settled into her RV seat she leaned over and picked up Charity's book.

I was sold. Any book that captured my wife's attention and encouraged her in her homeschool journey like this one did was a book I wanted to get into the hands of other moms.

So, Familyman Ministries is pleased to present you with the novel, "The Homeschool Experiment." Within these pages, you will meet a normal mother of normal children facing a normal, chaotic year of trying to figure out what it means to homeschool and love her family.

It's not always pretty…and that's why my wife likes this book. It tells it like it is and serves as a reminder that she's not alone in her struggles and frustrations. When you read it from someone else's perspective, it helps you to laugh and see things more clearly.

That's my hope for you, the reader, that when you close this book you'll know what matters most. Our desire is that this book will spark some great conversations in your homeschool circles as well (to help you, we've included some discussion questions in the back).

You've heard enough from me. Let me introduce you to Julianne Miller, who is sure to become a good friend. You're going to love her Homeschool Experiment.

—Todd Wilson
"The Familyman"
Familyman Ministries

# 2010 Homeschool Convention Shopping List

**Daniel** (6 years old, First Grade)

- Phonics/spelling
- Math
- anything else ?

**Joy** (4 years old, Preschool)

- Preschool workbook
- anything else?

**Baby Michael**

- What do I do with him during school?

**Wal-Mart**

- diapers
- milk
- toilet paper
- Diet Coke

Julianne Miller

# ~ May ~

"Hello. May I help you?" asks the woman at the first booth I approach in the noisy Oklahoma City Convention Hall. She is wearing a pink sweater set and a string of pearls.

"Um, yes, I was just wondering about—well—I mean, what is Classical Advantage?" I ask, reading the banner above her head. I want my children to have an advantage. Don't I?

"We are a group of homeschoolers that meets each week to do our classical memory work together." The woman beams at me. "Here is what we will cover in Section 8 next year."

She hands me a flyer and I read:

History—Ancient Greece to the Fall of Rome
Latin—Declensions
Math—Geometric Formulas
Grammar—Prepositions and Diagramming

My head swims. Wait a second—this must be for highschoolers. Whew!

"Oh, sorry!" I laugh. "My son will only be in first grade and my daughter will be in preschool. Where's that level?"

"Actually, your son and daughter are still in the Grammar stage," the woman explains, gesturing to a thick binder, "so they *would* be memorizing this material. You'd be amazed at how well the kids do and how much they like it."

She pushes a laptop toward me. "Here's one of our four-year-old students."

She clicks on the YouTube video, and I see a cute girl in pigtails lisping, "Alexander the Great, the son of Philip of Macedon, was born in 356 BC. He used his tactical prowess to wage a series of successful military campaigns in Asia Minor, eventually conquering Persia and expanding the Macedonian Empire."

Oh, that's funny! This is sort of a strange place for a joke, but clearly it can't be…I mean…a four-year-old? That girl can't really have memorized—

The lady is waiting for my reaction. Okay, I think this is for real.

"Wow, impressive," I say weakly. The pigtailed girl is now twirling around in a circle with her arms out saying, "Latin noun endings, first declension: -*a*, -*ae*, -*ae*, -*arum*, -*ae*, -*is*, -*am*, -*as*, -*a*, -*is*."

"But, ah, do you think she knows what she's saying?"

"That's actually not our focus at this age," the woman explains to me, as if she's heard that question many times. "We're just filling the mind full of information. Kids this age love to learn facts and parrot them back. The understanding comes later, in the Logic and Rhetoric stages."

"Uh-huh. Okay, well, I'll take this flyer and think about it. Thanks very much!" As I slip away, I hear the girl's mom on the video coaching her, "Now, Campbell, can you say your South African Rivers?"

Seriously? My four-year-old still has long conversations with her stuffed animals and can't remember that Monday comes before Tuesday. If I have to teach her Latin declensions, I'm pretty sure my head will explode.

Where are the booths for normal children? I scan desperately around the crowded convention hall. Where are the people who tell me what to do with my six-year-old boy when he would rather play LEGOs than read, much less memorize South African Rivers?

I spot another booth with a large cardboard book for its sign. On the book's cover, hand-painted letters crookedly spell out, "A Natural Education." That sounds nice.

Okay, I don't exactly know what that means, but I like natural things. Like trees. Sky. And…education?

There's a rumpled-looking man in glasses and a polka-dot bow tie waiting for me.

"Hello!" I say. "What sort of things do you recommend for first-grade boys?"

"First grade?" he says sharply, looking at me as if I'd asked him what sort of body piercings he would recommend for children of that age. "Just let them play!"

"No, er, I mean for *school*," I explain. This is a homeschool convention, is it not?

"No need for 'school,'" he says, making quotation marks in the air with his hands. "Just read to him. Don't waste his time on meaningless busywork, like filling in worksheets. Take him on nature walks! Let him build forts in the living room! Let him race cars on ramps on your stairs! When my children were six and eight, they built a castle out of tree branches in the backyard and played in it every day for months!"

"Really? How did you mow your lawn?"

"Oh, we didn't worry about the lawn! Which is more important—allowing your children's imagination to grow and flourish or having your grass cut?"

"Um, the imagination one," I say, though I think my husband, John, would beg to disagree. The one time I persuaded him to let the grass grow so our backyard would be "more like the country," we got a grass snake and lots of angry weeds. He likes a nice, neat lawn.

"Right!" the man says triumphantly. "Here, you need this." He presses a spiral-bound booklet into my hands. "These are the books to read to your son."

"Actually, I have three children. I also have a daughter who's four and a baby who's one, and I—"

"Wonderful! Start them early! Read to them three hours every day if you can. The books listed here in bold are the ones you *must* read, and all the others are ones you *have* to read. It's only seven dollars."

"Okay," I say, pulling out a twenty. I could use a list of great books, plus I don't think he'll take no for an answer. As he makes change, I flip the booklet open. There must be a thousand books listed in here!

Ages 5–8:

*Treasure Island,* unabridged

*Oliver Twist,* unabridged

*Swiss Family Robinson,* unabridged

I'm sure these are great and all, but Daniel barely listens to an entire Bible story without falling off the couch. I don't think we're ready for Dickens. On the other hand, I don't want illiterate children. I'll give it a shot.

"Thank you." I take the booklet and slip it into my convention tote. "Now, what about, you know, phonics and math and stuff?"

"Wait until he's nine." The man waves his hand in the air. "At least. Just read—give him great literature—it will cover everything. He'll pick up reading on his own. No need to have him write yet. And for math, he can count pinecones and acorns."

"Uh-huh." I say. "Okay, thanks!" I back away imagining what John might say if I told him we were just going to read and count acorns for school next year. Right. Perhaps A Natural Education is not the best plan for us either.

I'm starting to get a headache, but I can't give up. I *have* to find something that will work! I see a cute family—parents with eight children trailing behind, in matching jumpers (girls) and vests (boys), like ten adorable homeschool ducks. Everyone seems to have it all together. How have I been doing this for nearly two years and still don't know what I'm doing? Last year was Daniel's kindergarten year, so it wasn't too bad, but first grade is starting to feel overwhelming to me.

I try to ignore the pounding in my head. There has *got* to be a curriculum that is fun to do but will still give the kids a great education. I look up, and in the middle of the convention center, I see it: An immense, gauze butterfly suspended above a circular booth. Under the butterfly a banner reads: "Exploring God's Creation—A Hands-On Curriculum." This must be it! I make my way over.

"Can I help you?" asks a middle-aged woman in a khaki skirt. She looks nice. Like an experienced mom who knows what I should do.

"Yes, I hope so. I've got a first grader, a preschooler, and a baby—well, really he'll be a toddler—and I don't know where to start, and I don't know what to do with each of them, and what about my toddler?" I realize I sound a bit panicked, so I take a deep breath. "Could you tell me about your program, please?"

She smiles calmly at me, "Oh, I've got just the thing for you. What we have is a curriculum that is very hands-on so your toddler would be in the high chair while you and your first grader make a cookie map of ancient Egypt. Then you'll frost the cookie and put on the Nile River in sparkly, blue frosting.

"Another day you'll make a clay pot with homemade play dough. Then you'll weave river reeds together and pound them flat to make papyrus, and then your son will write Egyptian hieroglyphics on the papyrus and put it in the pot. He'll be practicing fine motor skills, handwriting, history—everything rolled into one."

I don't know how Daniel would handle writing hieroglyphics, considering he still reverses an occasional *s* or *j* in the regular old English alphabet. And I'm not quite sure where I'd find river reeds to weave together. Other than that though, this sounds great.

I picture us in the kitchen making our little clay pots. I'd be wearing my Williams Sonoma flowered apron, and Joy and Michael would be playing with the play dough. We'd probably be listening to Mozart. And how fantastic to learn all about ancient Egypt! Daniel would be so advanced!

"Okay!" Exploring God's Creation sounds like a lot of fun, and this friendly lady seems so sure it would work well for us. "How much is it?"

"Well, you would need Grade 1 SuperCore, and that includes your teacher's notes and planner, a phonics and reading program, a history notebook and timeline, an ant farm for science, and seeds to start your own garden. Oh, and counters and Unifix cubes for math manipulatives…"

I actually have no idea what Unifix cubes are, but everyone keeps talking about them, so they must be important. I am nodding my head and tune back in as she finishes:

"…All that together is only $459, but we offer a 10 percent discount for convention attendees, and you don't pay shipping of course, so it's a wonderful deal. Now remember, your preschooler can do this too, so everyone is covered. We accept check, cash, or debit card."

Four *hundred* and fifty-nine dollars? For first grade? I can only imagine the look on John's face if he heard that. But, this *is* our children's education we're talking about. If we enrolled them in Redbud Academy, the tuition would be way more than this. Really, this is a bargain!

"I need to talk it over with my husband first," I tell her. "But I'm very interested. Thank you so much!"

I just have to sit down and think for a minute. And I need a Diet Coke.

*****

"Hey, Lisa, can I join you?" I ask, as I plop my convention tote on the table in the convention hall's food court. Lisa and I drove here together from Tulsa this morning. She's got seven kids—all sweet little things—and has been homeschooling forever, so she pretty much knows everything. She still likes to come to the convention, though, to hear the speakers and get motivated for the next year.

"Sure," she says. "I need a break from this catalog anyway. My head's starting to hurt." Lisa sets down the Sonlight catalog, pushes her glasses up on top of her curly black hair, and rubs her eyes.

"Oh, man, no kidding." I twist open my three-dollar bottle of Diet Coke and massage my temples. "I'm totally confused now. That Exploring God's Creation program looks really good, but it's like four hundred dollars, and I'm not sure if it's exactly right. Then, this other man said I just need to read to them a lot and let them play. But then am I a slacker if I'm not teaching them Latin? *Should* I be teaching them Latin?"

"Do you want to teach them Latin?" Lisa asks.

"Uh, no." Is that a trick question? "I think if I can do the basics and keep my sanity, I'll be doing well. But I'm not even sure what the basics are anymore. Don't I have to do math in first grade?"

"Well, I'll tell you what I think," Lisa begins.

I settle back and help myself to some of Lisa's nachos. I wish I could download the entire contents of her brain into mine, but this is a start.

"You have to do what works for you. There is no way that you can do what everyone says you *should* do. No school can either, by the way. You have to choose an approach that fits your personality and works for your children. You can't feel guilty about what you choose not to do. Some of my friends love the structure of the Classical approach. It makes me break out in hives.

"Then the whole hands-on thing—I have friends, very organized and conscientious people, who did the kindergarten program and *loved* it. They are the kinds of people who have clean closets and can follow directions well. Or they have one child. I am not such a person.

"I bought that hands-on curriculum back when I only had three kids. I remember the time we were supposed to be making a pot out of homemade play dough. Hannah was tired of being in her high chair since we had just finished breakfast, so she was whining. While I was trying to keep her happy, Jonah dropped the entire bag of flour, and it puffed up in a huge white cloud. The whole kitchen was covered in flour, but I was determined to keep going. Then Sarah spilled her juice, which mixed with the flour and turned everything into sticky clumps of yellow paste. Without thinking, I told the kids to go to the other room, so they did, but they walked *right through the mess* and tracked gooey footprints into the living room.

"I had to put the baby in a sling, because she was screaming at that point. I was thinking, 'Why in the world did I not buy Play-Doh at Walmart?' Anyway, the kids ended up watching *Mr. Rogers* and *Reading Rainbow* while I finished mopping the kitchen and vacuuming the living room. Then I was so tired, and the baby was so cranky that I put us all in the car, and we went on a little road trip to Sonic."

"Isn't Sonic the best?" I break in. "And McDonald's. I mean, I feel like such a bad mom for saying it, but it's true! When everyone's stressed out, the baby can go to sleep, the kids can have chicken nuggets, and I can listen to NPR and get a Diet Coke."

"I know!" Lisa says, with wide eyes. "McDonald's breakfasts – you drive up and give them money, and they just *hand you food*! Pancakes, piping hot! Nothing to clean up, people strapped in their seats, and you get to sit there and eat. Such a lovely thing. Of course, now," she wrinkles her nose, "with seven kids and me, it's like twenty dollars for breakfast, so we don't go there so much."

Ooh, that's something to consider. The more kids I have, the less McDonald's I'll be able to afford. I make a mental note to think about that later. And what about Starbucks? It's already getting expensive, what with my latte and the kids' vanilla milks, and then Daniel always wants a piece of banana chocolate chip coffee cake, and Joy always wants a slice of pumpkin loaf. So I get it for them. Is that so wrong? Anyway…homeschooling. Yes, where were we?

"I learned that I'd rather teach my kids a couple of basic lessons and then be done with school for the day," Lisa is saying. "Simple works best for me. I mean, when a curriculum says 'hands-on,' think about whose hands they mean. Yours. And my hands are pretty busy, so the less extra work they have to do, the better. In fact, my kids are pretty good at coming up with their own hands-on projects, if I give them some cardboard boxes and masking tape.

"We did projects when they were young, but not every day," Lisa continues. "You really don't have to cover ancient Egypt in first grade unless you feel like it, or are one of those legendary people whose toddlers are perfectly behaved while the older kids do school. It was just too much work for me, honestly."

Well, this is good to hear. If Supermom says it was too much work for her, I'm guessing it might be tough for me as well. "So what did you do?"

"Well, I resold my entire curriculum at a homeschool used-book fair, and got half the money back, and then I went to Mardel and bought a first-grade math workbook and a first-grade spelling workbook. We did those, and read library books, *a lot* of library books."

Saying Lisa likes to read is like saying Siberia can get chilly. She had to get a library card for each of her kids when they were toddlers, because the Tulsa library *only* lets you check out fifty books at a time on each card, and she pushes her books in a stroller because carrying them all in a bag throws out her back. If she's reading a good book, it can be three o'clock in the afternoon before she remembers details like lunch.

Lisa goes on, "But, remember, you do have a six-year-old boy. His attention span is short, and he probably won't sit still very well. Put in lots of breaks so the kids can play, but an hour of seatwork during the whole day won't hurt Daniel."

"Okay, but that man told me that worksheets will ruin Daniel's brain!"

Lisa snorts. "Then all our brains would be ruined, right? We all did worksheets. Look, I'm not saying do them four hours a day, but a book to give you guidance on what you should be teaching your children isn't a bad thing. I bought cheap a math and spelling workbook, but any standard one would work – Saxon, A Beka, Bob Jones. The kids are going to have to learn how to sit at a desk and write at some point. You're teaching self-control as much as anything. Sitting still and doing what Mom says is a big part of what they're learning here."

"What about science and history? Do I need a separate curriculum?" I have so much to figure out.

"Well, what we do is—wait. You don't need to think about that yet. Just start with the basics: Bible, reading, phonics/spelling, and math. Simpler is better at the beginning. Plan on three twenty minute sessions a day. Once you and the kids are in a good routine, you can add more."

"Okay," I sigh. "But what if I completely mess up first grade? What if I ruin Daniel for life?"

"Oh, well, at least you're not blowing things out of proportion." Lisa says with a raised eyebrow. "Jules, look how well you did this past year, even with a new baby to take care of! You taught Daniel to read, when he was *four*, no less."

"Well, he pretty much picked it up on his own..." I protest.

"No, you worked with him a lot, and then he picked it up. You taught him phonics, and checked out those phonics books at the library, and practiced three-letter short-vowel words in the grocery store. I remember."

Oh yeah. That's true. I guess I did.

"And you kept working on his handwriting with him even when *Handwriting Without Tears* turned into many, many tears," she points out.

True. Every time I made him sit down with a pencil, Daniel felt that the world was full of injustice. Even with the best curriculum, we still had lots of tears. Lots of phone calls to Lisa after those mornings.

"And you read Joy all those beautiful *Five in a Row* picture books and helped her finger paint. Oh, and let's not forget— nursed and diapered and took care of Michael."

This is true also. Why do I doubt myself so much? I need Lisa to come live in my house and be my cheerleader.

Or maybe she could come over and teach my kids. That would be awesome!

But no, her seven children might miss her. So I guess it's up to me.

"You'll be fine," Lisa promises me. "Here, let me pray for you, then you can go buy your stuff."

"That would be great," I sigh, feeling so much better already.

*"Father, we thank you for our precious children who you have entrusted to us. We pray for wisdom as you guide us. Help us to know what's best for each of them and for our families. I pray you would help Julianne trust in your guidance and know that 'all of her children would be taught by the Lord and great would be the peace of her children.' Help us follow you faithfully, even though we, like Abraham, might not know where we are going. You do. Thank you, Lord. Amen."*

I am crying now, sniffling and wiping my nose. I am such a crier. Lisa laughs at me and finds a tissue in the bottomless bag she always has. "Now, go buy your stuff. Have fun."

"Yeah, right," I say. Okay, maybe it will be a little fun.

"Call me when you're ready for dinner," Lisa says, and she returns to eating nachos and circling books in her catalog.

*****

After the conference, Lisa and I eat dinner at a Mexican restaurant. (We seem to consume vast quantities of cheese and chocolate whenever we get together.) Then we get stuck in a traffic jam on the turnpike back to Tulsa, so we get lots of extra kid-free time to talk. I pick up my car from her house and drive home. I'm thinking over the day and all the decisions I've had to make.

It certainly would be easier if John and I would enroll our kids at Redbud Academy, the sweet private Christian school down the street from us. Lots of our friends send their children there, and those kids seem to be doing so well; they are polite, darling, literate children. I'd love to have my kids turn out like that. Why am I doing this homeschooling thing again?

Oh, right, John wanted me to try it. He has so few strong opinions, but go figure, he had an opinion about homeschooling. Something in me wants to try it too. So I'll try it. If it doesn't work out, Redbud is a good Plan B.

I've kept a list of all my purchases.

Daniel
- Math workbook $19
- Math speed drills $5
- Spelling and poetry workbook (A Beka) $29
- Reading book (A Beka) $19
- Grammar (Rod and Staff) $8
- Botany (Apologia) $30
- Unifix cubes $16
- Human anatomy puzzle (Melissa & Doug) $19
- Easy reader books - I'll get at the used-book fair

Joy
- Numbers workbook (Rod and Staff) $3
- Letter workbook (Rod and Staff) $3
- Math: teddy bears $20
- Science: butterfly house $20
  *(Lisa said fennel attracts butterflies.)*
- Pegs with shapes (Laurie) $10
- Wooden pattern blocks $15

Michael
- Ball (He needs a present too!) $5

John
- *Help! I'm Married to a Homeschooling Mom!* book $10

**Total Cost: $231**

Not bad! I think my accountant husband will be impressed.

Thinking about all this fun new stuff is cheering me up. Next year is going to be great! I'm still going to let the kids play in the backyard, go on nature walks, do wonderful imaginative things, and help me in the kitchen. I just want to make sure they can read, write, and count as well as—okay, better than—other kids.

And get admitted to Harvard. Not that they'd *want* to go there, but it would be nice to have the option. Also, I wouldn't complain if one of them were a Rhodes Scholar. I'd like to visit Oxford.

And really—how hard can first grade be? We did okay with kindergarten, as Lisa pointed out.

I was my high school valedictorian and a National Merit Scholar. I graduated from college with honors and had a successful career in the business world for five years. I can surely manage first grade and preschool. Last year was just hard because of the baby and sleep deprivation.

This whole homeschooling thing is going to be a piece of cake.

# Let's have a ball!

What: Michael's 1st birthday
Where: The Millers' House
When: Friday, June 11
        12-2 p.m.

No gifts please –
your presence is enough!

R.S.V.P. to Julianne

# ~ June ~

At least the boys are having fun. I'm in the backyard with my kids and their cousins, Maddie and Drew. Drew is a few months older than Daniel; Maddie's ten but she thinks she's sixteen and seems bored by everything.

"What are we supposed to *do*?" she asks, after giving our backyard a once-over.

"Whatever you want!" I smile cheerily at her. "You can draw with chalk or jump on the trampoline, or play with Joy." Joy is cooking for her dogs, Bis-kette and Dee-Dee, in her playhouse.

"You could play with the boys on the fort." I knew she wouldn't go for that one. The boys, as usual, are playing a game involving shooting things and whacking each other with sticks. They usually get a bit wild, and their games often end in tears. "Or you can sit here and talk with us!"

"Yeah, right." Maddie snorts and rolls her eyes. "I'll go text some of my friends." She finds a chair on the side of the patio, plops down, and buries herself in her iPhone.

I can't believe her parents gave her an iPhone. *I* don't even know how to use an iPhone. Granted, I'm the most technologically backward person I know and have no desire to use phones for anything other than calling people, but still. "You still don't know how to text?" my friends are always asking. Yes, well. I have lived thirty-four years without texting and seem to be managing.

John's brother, Dave, and his wife, Ginger, drove up from Dallas with Maddie and Drew for Michael's party. I have to admit I was a little surprised. They usually can't be bothered with such minutia, but I guess since we haven't seen them since Christmas, they decided to come. John's parents, Frank and Vicky, also came up from Highland Park, their exclusive neighborhood in the heart of Dallas. John's family is very, well, um… rich. And mine is…not so much. The family dynamics can get a bit strange, but mostly everyone gets along.

My parents flew in from Midland, way out in West Texas, and my sister, Holly, is on her way up from Austin. Texas will be well represented at the party.

*None* of Michael's three baby friends who we invited could come, and all of our family (who I mostly invited as a formality) decided to come. If I would have known that, I might have put a little more thought into the party. John's family is used to the over-the-top birthday parties that people throw in Highland Park. Oh well.

At least John cleaned up the backyard for the occasion. It's always covered in trash that the kids commandeer for their imaginary stories. Daniel wouldn't let John clean up a big tangled ball of string hanging from the pear tree because it's his "net for catching robot bears." He and Joy have involved battles with these robot bears.

"All right, I'll leave the net," John said earlier as he looked around, as if seeing the back patio for the first time. He's been working a lot, so he actually hasn't been out here much.

"Why are there diaper boxes all over the patio? This is ridiculous." He started picking them up.

"No, Daddy! Wait!" Daniel's blue eyes widened in alarm. "Those are for my secret hideout!" He is a type A personality and builds things constantly, which is great for his imagination and all, but slightly annoying when we have to take his creation apart, and he starts freaking out.

"Can I at least move them to the side of the house?" John asked me.

"Yes, that's fine," I said, giving Daniel a look, since I could tell he was about to protest. "Guys, help Daddy move these over by the fence. And move the rocket too, okay?" The "rocket" is an old refrigerator box with fire drawn on the bottom and a window cut out of the side.

"Yes, ma'am," Daniel muttered but dropped his head and looked as woeful as if his dog had just died. He's a bit dramatic.

"Great," John said, as the boxes were hauled off. "That's better. Except for that pole. Can I get rid of it yet?"

The pole is part of a basketball goal that we got for free a few years ago. At the time, I thought it would be great to set it up but have since realized we have nowhere to put it. Plus, the backboard kept giving us fiberglass splinters. The pole is lying on the ground behind the shed and the kids have been using it as a balance beam, which actually works quite well, since the huge cylinder of concrete around the base holds it in place.

"The kids use it as their balance beam," I said weakly, realizing I sounded a lot like Daniel.

"Honey, they can use plenty of other things as a balance beam. They can walk on the railroad ties or the curb or the crack in the sidewalk. Or, you know, the *actual* balance beam at their *actual* gymnastics class that we are paying for?"

"Okay. That's fine," I said quickly. I was willing to sacrifice the pole so we didn't have to discuss the cost of their gymnastics classes again. "But, it's behind the shed anyway, so no one will see it today. Look how good the yard looks, honey!" John looked around and decided it was acceptable.

Now, I survey the yard again and must say, it does look pretty great. The yellow roses along the back fence are in full bloom. I guess it was worth scratching my arms bloody on their thorns when I planted them last spring. The grass is green and freshly mowed and our cute, raised-bed garden is leafy with spinach and lettuce and beans. Actually, the arugula is getting a bit wilted now with the June heat, but still, it looks very organic of us. My sister will be proud.

Ever since her daughter was born nine months ago, my sister, Holly, has been in a health-nut-mommy-blogger phase. Where is she anyway? Her plane was supposed to have landed at 10:45. Gardening was not something Holly and I ever learned in Midland, out in the flat, cracked desert of West Texas. Midland was perpetually dry and hot, so when I first saw Tulsa's green trees and rolling hills I fell in love.

Vivaldi's *Four Seasons* could easily have been inspired by Northeastern Oklahoma. Spring crashes in with thunderstorms of light and glory. Tornado sirens send us scurrying to eat our dinner in the closet, and then months of tree blossoms erupt overnight—each morning as I drive down the street, I see gifts anew. Summer nights lilt along, warm and slow; I sit watching my husband and children chase fireflies through the darkening yard. In the fall, the horizon shimmers with leafy flames of gold and scarlet: maples, Bradford pears, sweet gums. And, in the winter, when the snow gusts past the bony branches of the sycamore trees, I can cuddle inside with my family by firelight and candle-glow, like a cozy picture on a blue Delft Christmas plate.

Because I grew up in Midland, where the seasons alternated between hot with green grass and warm with brown grass, I'm continually astonished by the changing seasons. I'm shocked and gasping when we drive down the streets in the spring: "Look at that tree! Oh, guys, look out Joy's window; look at that pink dogwood! It's just *gorgeous!*"

Right now, Joy is still busily cooking imaginary food in her playhouse, periodically interrupting Maddie's texting to ask if she wants invisible pancakes or an invisible ham sandwich for lunch. Maddie is at least doing her part by ordering and pretending to eat, which is uncharacteristically involved of her. Dave and Frank are over on the corner of the patio, probably wishing they had a stiff drink. John brought them Dr Peppers.

I'm here at the table with Ginger and Vicky. There are some benefits to having so many adults around. My parents are in the house to hear Michael when he wakes up from his nap, so I am just sitting here with nothing to do. It's great.

Vicky watches the kids play for a bit, and then asks casually, "So, Julianne, are you tired of homeschooling yet? Or ... ?" She lets the question hang, hoping I'll jump in. I don't. "Or…are you going to keep going?"

Here we go again. I try to not sigh. "No, we're going to do it again next year." I force a smile, bracing myself for what's coming.

"I just don't know how you do it with three kids!" Vicky says, looking worried for me, or maybe for the kids. "It seems so hard!"

"It was, especially with a new baby, but it was a good year too." The homeschool support group I'm in has lots of women with four, eight, or even ten kids, and all those women are still alive. I want to tell Vicky this, but I don't. That will only scare her even more.

"You know," Vicky adds, biting her lower lip, "my friend volunteers at a junior high. She was telling me that a seventh-grader recently enrolled after being homeschooled. She said he was way behind academically."

I'm waiting, thinking she has a point. Nope, I guess that's it.

"And she said he was behind socially too." Vicky shakes her head sadly.

These comments are *so* helpful. Thanks, Vicky, for that vote of confidence. You don't even know that kid, and yet he's your benchmark, rather than all the homeschooled kids who are above average? Breathe. Smile.

"Yes," I say, as politely as I can manage. "I'm sure that happens sometimes. Excuse me, I'm going to get a few things ready inside."

As I get up, Vicky and Ginger start discussing Dalton Prep, the private school that Maddie and Drew attend. At least Vicky is happy about that.

Even though I'm used to Vicky's comments, I'm still annoyed by them. I go into the kitchen and get out plates and forks, slamming them down on the counter a little harder than I intend.

What Vicky doesn't understand is how all this talk of how hard homeschooling is, how I can quit any time, all of this makes me even more determined to do it. I have a slight stubborn streak. And I like to prove people wrong.

I think of the time my fourth-grade teacher told me Longfellow's *Paul Revere's Ride* was too long to memorize. Within the next two weeks, I had memorized all one hundred and thirty lines of it and recited it to her at recess, just to prove I could. It irritates me when people say I can't do something.

Okay, deep breaths, Julianne. Vicky isn't saying you're a bad mother; she's only wanting the best for her grandchildren. Vicky and Ginger are nice women who love their families. We are all on the same team here.

After calming down a bit, I go outside with the plates and forks. Ginger and Vicky are discussing how exhausted they both are.

"Luisa had to take the week off last week, so I had the kids all day, every day!" Ginger is moaning.

Yes, welcome to my world.

"Oh, you poor thing!" Vicky commiserates. "I understand! Maria had to take care of her grandchildren, so I was stuck arranging everything for this trip, getting the house ready, everything all by myself!"

What, packing for two? Vicky has had Maria as her housekeeper for at least thirty years. In fact, both John and Dave invited Maria's family to their weddings. Even when her children were young, Vicky was always quite busy with her PTA projects and Junior League meetings and needed Maria at least four days a week. So I can see how details like laundry and packing might be a bit baffling to her.

Vicky looks dressed for a yacht trip right now, in her white-and-navy-striped boat shirt (Talbot's, I'm guessing) and navy capris. She's almost sixty but is one of those women who looks unfailingly put together and beautiful.

And thin. Annoyingly thin. Once we were visiting for Christmas, and all of us swore the scale was broken, but Vicky stepped on and chirped, "Nope. One hundred and seven, like always!"

Ginger always looks perfect too. I try not to hold it against her. Today, her long auburn hair is swirling around her shoulders; she's wearing huge fashionable sunglasses and diamond stud earrings.

I feel a bit frumpy next to them. I still have fifteen pounds to lose of Michael's baby weight. With the other two kids I tried to have the weight off by the first birthday party, but this time it didn't happen. Part of it is—I have no time to work out. Part of it is lack of sleep. And the rest—I don't know. I'll get there. It might just take me a little longer than planned. And, I have to remind myself, Vicky and Ginger have housekeepers, nannies, and this mysterious thing called Free Time. I do not.

"*Love* the Escalade!" Vicky is saying now. "Laura has one just like that!" "Laura" is Laura Bush, who lives near them and attends the same Methodist church. I doubt "Laura" would recognize Vicky by name, but Vicky manages to speak of her as if they were best friends.

"Yes, we love it too," Ginger says. "We needed more room. The kids were always fighting over which DVD to watch. This one has two DVD players so each of them can watch their own movie. We hardly heard a peep out of them the whole way up here! In fact, we are considering—gasp—*driving* to California this summer!"

"Hold on a minute, there," Dave interrupts as he and Frank walk up. "Nobody said anything about driving." John comes out the door with a plate of fruit to set on the table.

"I said con*sid*ering. We are *considering* it. I am, anyway. I detest flying. All that waiting in lines and keeping the kids quiet on the plane. Ugh."

"Oh, I totally agree." On this, Ginger and I are soul sisters. "Flying is the worst torture for parents. It's evil. If everything goes well, you're fine. But if something goes wrong and someone has a meltdown..."

"You're dead," Ginger finishes.

"Dead. It's over." I pour myself a Diet Coke. "The whole plane ride you are stuck with a screaming child and two hundred strangers who hate your guts. I've told you about my trip to Chicago, right?"

"What happened?" Vicky looks terrified. I think the thought of flying with one child without a nanny is horrifying enough to her.

"Total meltdown. I was five months pregnant with Joy; Daniel was about eighteen months old. We were going to watch John run the Chicago Marathon, but he was on a different flight so I had Daniel by myself. I don't think I had told Daniel 'no' or 'sit still' very much until that point. These were completely foreign concepts to him. Right after takeoff he started screaming his head off. The lady in front of us changed seats because he was kicking the back of her chair so much. He was literally on the floor for most of the flight. Businessmen were glaring at me. I felt awful. There's nothing you can do at that point."

"Nothing," Ginger echoes.

"A wonderful stranger ended up giving Daniel some cookies, which helped. Now, I'm prepared. I pack enough toys, DVDs, snacks, and drinks to last us for about three days. Just in case. I pack candy and cookies too, as a last resort."

"See, that's what I'm saying about flying!" Ginger tells Dave.

"Yeah, but driving? Do you know how many hours that is to California? It's probably two days," Dave argues.

"Two *days*? Oh." Ginger has never been very good at geography. She has a degree in Interior Design, but managed to get through high school and college without learning where those quiet states like Wisconsin or Idaho are. She never cared enough to figure it out.

"Where in California are you going?" John asks.

"Oh, Dave has this conference about—what is it, honey? Some accounting thing."

"Fraud."

"Right. Fraud. And since he's managing partner of his firm, he's decided to go," Ginger explains.

Dave is the older brother, and the first ten years out of college he practically gave up his life at a Big Eight accounting firm to get to the top. Even now, he puts in long hours and works weekends, something John doesn't want to do. John still does well, because he's a hard worker (and brilliant), but he isn't a partner like his older brother. Instead, he's the manager of the audit department at his firm. It's the choice he made.

Ginger continues, "So I thought the kids and I would tag along, go to Disneyland, lie on the beach. The town is close to Anaheim. Where is it again?"

"Dana Point?" John asks.

"Yes! That's it!" Ginger says. "How did you know that?"

How *did* my husband know that?

"Well, I forgot to tell you, Jules," John looks at me apologetically, "My boss asked if I'd want to go to that same conference. He wants me to represent the firm. Good networking, I guess."

Okay, these are the things I want to hear when I ask about his day. John "forgets" to tell me stuff all the time. I have to virtually pry it out of him. He is the quiet type, and he thinks no one would be interested in whatever he has to say. Small details like friends giving birth. People quitting. Trips to *California.*

"Okay, in the future," I say, trying not to nag him too much, especially in front of his family, "this is the sort of information I would like to know."

"I know, I know." John smiles at me with twinkling eyes. "So, wanna go?"

"Go where?" my mom asks, coming out of the house. She is holding Michael, who must have just woken up from his nap. His cheeks are rosy with sleep; his wispy, white-blonde hair is sticking out all crazily in the back, like a soft circle of dandelion fluff. Is there anything more endearing than a rumpled, nap-tender baby? Maybe a sleeping baby. Or maybe baby toes, like rows of perfect, tiny peas.

"Sweepy baby," I croon, scooping him up from my mom to cuddle him on my chest and kiss his warm cheeks. My dad hands over a sippy cup of milk. I snuggle Michael close to me. He peers out with eyes like big brown marbles, surveying all the activity.

"Where'd all these blonde kids come from?" Dad asks. It's so weird—John and I both have brown hair, but all three kids are blondies.

John is tall and handsome, and he always tells me I'm beautiful, but I'd say I'm about average. Our children, however, are absolutely adorable, like three stair-stepped angels, with their dimples and button noses and doe eyes. When they're in a good mood, that is. When they're in a bad mood, they have furrowed brows and scowls and fire shooting from their eyes. It all depends on the day, really.

John fills in my mom and dad about the conference.

"I want to go," I say, "but it's so much *work*. Vacations are so exhausting. They aren't vacations at all for the mom. They're just a week of stress in a new place preceded and followed by a week of laundry."

"That's the spirit, honey," John laughs.

"Well, it's true! I'll be the one taking care of the kids, keeping them quiet in the hotel room, listening to tired, cranky little people who miss their own beds."

"You need a nanny." Ginger reaches for some grapes from the fruit plate John brought out with him. "Seriously. Then she can watch them and you can go to the spa. The conference is at this swanky resort."

"St. Regis Monarch Beach," Dave jumps in. "The one where all the AIG employees went days after the federal bailout. There was a huge public backlash."

"I remember that!" John said. "But I didn't realize this is where it was."

"Yeah. It's seriously nice. Five-star luxury resort."

"Ooh," Vicky is suddenly interested. "You *should* go, Julianne. You could use a break."

What is that supposed to mean? Vicky acts like being a full-time mother is such a terrible, exhausting job, as though she thinks I must be on the edge of a nervous breakdown at all times.

"At places like that they usually have babysitters on staff," Ginger tells me. "You can leave the kids in your room, and the babysitter keeps them busy. Last time Dave and I went to New York, we hardly even saw the kids except at breakfast."

Like I'm going to leave my kids in a hotel room with some person I've never met.

"But I like my kids. I want do things with them if we go," I protest.

"I *like* my kids too!" Ginger bristles. Oh shoot, now I've offended her. "I'm just *saying*, it's a nice break, that's all."

"Jules, think of all the educational opportunities!" My mom is setting the table for pizza. "You could go to a museum, take the kids on a boat trip. When Dad and I went to Catalina Island, they had dolphin- and whale-watching cruises. You could count it as science."

Now that sounds awesome. Plus, it sounds a lot more fun than doing phonics and math at home.

We could do all kinds of educational things there. Forget about Disneyland. We could learn about oceanography, the history of westward expansion, Spanish missions in California. This could count as a *month* of school!

"Mom, I'm *star*ving!" Daniel comes up with a red, sweaty face, and Drew follows him. "And I'm so thirsty. Can you get me some milk? I'm *so* thirsty!" Have I mentioned Daniel is dramatic?

"Yes, good idea!" I say to Daniel. "The juice boxes are on the island in the kitchen. Can you go get them and give one to each of the kids, please? That would be a nice way to serve your sister and cousins." I'm trying to have Joy and Daniel do more things for themselves and for other people instead of expecting to be waited on all the time. The thought that they can do things for themselves doesn't seem to occur to them.

"I want Sprite," Drew whines.

"No, honey. You have juice like the other kids," Ginger answers.

"Mom, we have Sprite at home all the time!" Maddie chimes in from across the patio. "We *always* have Sprite. We're not babies."

"Fine!" Ginger says. "But you'll have to pour it yourself."

"Way to hold the line, babe," Dave says.

Ginger shoots him a look. "They whine so *much*! I'm so tired of the whining! Do yours do that?" she asks me.

"Yeah," I say. "Sometimes they do." Especially when I give in to them, I think. But I better not say that. She's already annoyed at me.

"Julianne, the pizza's probably about done," my mom jumps in. "Are we almost ready to eat?"

"Yeah, we're going to have to go ahead. We can't wait for Holly anymore. Would you mind bringing it out?" My kids are sort of like time bombs, especially Daniel. If he doesn't eat every few hours, he melts down. He turns into this sullen, angry child. We call it a Hunger Crash. Joy has Tired Crashes. I can see the storm clouds brewing on their faces. If we know what's good for us we'd better feed these children.

Just then I hear a "Knock, knock!" from inside the house. My sister is coming through the front door. She joins us on the patio, giving Mom a hug on the way out.

Holly's mahogany hair is pulled back in a low ponytail. She's wearing Emma in a chic, paisley-patterned Moby sling. I tried to use those with all three of my babies, but I always felt like the baby was squashed up inside or about to fall out. I could never pull it off.

On Holly the sling looks perfect, though. She looks like a celebrity mom out for a trip to the Farmer's Market with her adorable matching baby.

"Sorry I'm late!" she chirps. "I had to pick up a few things at Whole Foods on the way here. But don't let me interrupt! Let's eat!"

John starts handing out pizza, and my mom gets Michael settled in his outdoor high chair. (We eat lunch outside a lot so we have an outdoor seat as well as an indoor one.)

"I just brought a few things for Emma," Holly says in a low tone to me while everyone's getting food. "We don't let her have pizza yet, so I got some tofu and baby food. I usually hate to buy baby food, but what are you gonna do?" she says, laughing.

Indeed. I hate that store-bought baby food too. Which is why we feed our baby pizza.

*****

We sing "Happy Birthday" to Michael, who seems cheerfully confused by all the fuss, and he grins at all of us until John helps him blow out his candle. The kids made him carrot-applesauce cake—they saw it on *SuperWhy!* —and he gobbles it up. By the time he's done, he's got cream-cheese frosting and chocolate ice cream in his hair, but he's blissfully content. Then, he opens presents, with help from Daniel and Joy.

Dave and Ginger's gift is a Baby LeapPad, which is supposed to "give him a head start." Because I guess babies need a head start in computing or perhaps in texting their little baby friends. And they give him a one-hundred-dollar bill. For "whatever he wants."

Frank and Vicky give him a Jeep. A tiny, motorized version. They had it shipped to the Toys"R"Us here and picked it up when they got into town. Fabulous. He can drive around the neighborhood with his peeps.

Holly gives him a necklace of amber teething beads. "They release calming oils into the skin and help with teething," she said. "The oil is a natural painkiller. Emma's seemed to really help."

"Oh, look at that," my dad drawls when we put the necklace on. "Our little hippie!"

John doesn't seem too pleased with the hippie comparison, but I think Michael looks cute. Like a miniature surfer dude.

Daniel and Joy give Michael a special book: They collected pictures of family and familiar things around the house like a sippy cup, balls, and LEGOs (Daniel added that one), and then pasted the pictures onto construction paper. I covered the pages with contact paper, punched holes in them, and tied the book together with a ribbon. Daniel and Joy loved making something special, and Michael seems to love looking at all the familiar faces and toys.

My parents give him a cute wooden wagon for blocks. Into the wood is carved his name, then: "Happy First Birthday! Love, Poppy and Nana." Michael's present from John and me is a Little Tykes basketball goal, since he is obsessed with every kind of ball. That's one of the three words he can say. "Mah" for Momma and milk, "Da" for Daddy, and "bah" for ball. After John assembles it, Michael makes him and my dad play "bah," which means John and my dad shoot the ball and Michael claps and makes the sign for "more."

So much for the no gifts request on the invitation! No, I'm delighted everyone cared enough to come, and it's fine that they brought gifts. I might have to give the Baby LeapPad away, though. We have a policy of no video games, and already Daniel and Joy have said, "Why does Michael get a video game? It's not fair!"

After the party and a few more hours of hanging out, Dave and Ginger head off to the Radisson so Maddie and Drew can go swimming. Frank and Vicky leave for the McBirney Mansion, the historic local inn where they're staying. I'm sitting in the kitchen with Holly and Dad and Mom while John puts the kids to bed.

"Whew! I'm exhausted!" I say, sinking back into the kitchen couch. Any kind of party wears me out, but especially draining are parties that involve babies, cake, and the extended Miller family.

"Barb, where's my BlackBerry?" My dad looks around the kitchen. "I need to see what Light Sweet closed at today."

"Check the carry-on bag." My mom starts bagging up the leftover pizza.

My dad goes out to the living room. He is in oil, like most everyone in Midland, Texas. Or, the "awl bidness" as he says it, in his West Texas drawl. Dad checks the price of West Texas Intermediate light sweet crude like most people check the weather.

My mom starts wiping down the counters and waves me away as I start to get up and help, "Sweetie, you relax. I'll clean up." Bless her.

"Could you come live here?" I ask her. "Then the kitchen would be clean all the time."

"Oh, you do a good job. It's clean enough. It's hard with three little people in it all day long."

"No kidding," I say. "I fantasize about sending them all off to school so I can clean the house and have it stay clean for more than twenty minutes."

"Someday your house will stay clean, but you'll miss holding your babies. It will come soon enough." My mom starts to tear up. She always does that.

"Mom! No making us cry today!" I say reproachfully. I get emotional on birthdays. Last year our neighbor cut down a gorgeous sweet gum tree on Joy's fourth birthday and I bawled. "We walked by that tree every *day* when she was a baby!" I sobbed to John. "And now it's gone! It's like the death of her *childhood!*" He wonders where the kids get their emotional streaks.

"Are you glad to have a break from school?" asks Holly, thankfully changing the subject.

"Absolutely. I can't imagine being one of those people who homeschools through the summer. I was ready for the break. Last year was crazy—a new baby, a few trips, then the holidays, then John's busy season at work. I felt like we never got a chance to catch our breaths.

"I went to a homeschool convention last month, though, and bought all our curriculum, and this summer I'm going to get organized and ready to go. I think next year will be much better."

"I heard Daniel doing double-digit subtraction." My mom is loading the dishwasher. "He was saying something like, 'There are seventy-two robot bears and only sixty-three children, so there are nine more robot bears than children! They are doomed!' That's pretty good for just finishing kindergarten."

"That's so cute!" Holly says. "They are very creative. Joy was pretending to cook for me all afternoon. She said, 'Do you want pancakes or French toast?' and when I said, 'Pancakes, please,' she acted very serious and said, 'Oh, I'm so sorry. We're all out of pancakes. How about French toast?' She's a hoot."

"Yeah, somehow they manage to learn; I'm not sure how. Did you hear Vicky, though? Every time I see her, every single time, she says, 'Are you still homeschooling?' with this worried look on her face like I'm going to ruin all of us. She always says, 'You can quit any time, you know.'"

"It's because Vicky can't fathom homeschooling," Holly says. "It's not her thing."

"Yes, and ultimately, it doesn't matter what she thinks, if it's what you think God wants you to do," Mom says in her gentle way. "If I please men, I would not be a bondservant of

Christ." I know she is quoting Galatians 1:10; it's one of her favorite verses.

"I know, Mom. You're right. John thinks it would be good to homeschool and I want to try it too. It's just that Ginger is always talking about how fabulous Dalton Prep is, and Vicky thinks homeschooling is ridiculous. I feel like they are expecting me to fail. Or think I'm a freak."

"Which you are," Holly deadpans, and we all crack up. "Are you still boycotting Facebook, you weird girl?"

"Of course. Until the day I die. Why add one more time-sucking activity to my life? But look, I'm still here! You can still contact me in the form of an actual, real live person or by phone or by that old-fashioned method—email. I haven't vanished off the planet yet!"

"It's only a matter of time," Holly says. "So John was saying you might go to California! That's fun."

"Yes, and Mom was telling us about all the educational things to do there."

"Oooh, Jules!" Holly is getting an idea, I can tell. "I read this magazine article about a family that saved for, like, ten years, then took a whole year off and traveled the world. You could do that!"

"What could we do?" John asks, coming into the kitchen with Emma, asleep on his shoulder. He's so handsome when he's holding a baby.

"Oh yikes, she fell asleep on you?" Holly jumps up from her chair. "She must be exhausted. I'm going to go put her down. See you guys tomorrow." Holly slides Emma onto her shoulder and heads upstairs to the guest bedroom.

"'Night, Holly." I say. "I'll fill you in later," I tell John. This Traveling-the-World idea might be a bit of a discussion.

"We'd better hit the road too," Dad says, coming into the kitchen. "We'll come over in the morning."

"Sounds good," I said. "See you then. Thanks for coming!" We give hugs all around and see them out. John and I go to bed.

As I lie in bed, I am picturing all the places our family could go on our trip around the world. I think Holly's plan is completely feasible.

John and I have been saving two hundred dollars a month in an educational account in case we decide to put the kids in private school. If I end up homeschooling, we could use that for our educational travel account. We could visit our friends who are missionaries in Kenya, or China, or France. Our kids could learn about other cultures while learning to serve the people there.

I was listening to the Rick Steves radio show the other day, and he was discussing a web site where you can rent houses abroad. There was one in Scotland that cost only eight hundred dollars a month! That would be completely within our budget.

You know, over the course of the kids' education we'd probably *save* money over private school. Private school would cost thousands of dollars a year for all three of them. This would be way less than that.

Oh wait. What about John's job?

He couldn't get off for a month at a time to travel. Maybe he could travel with us to our destination, and then the kids and I could stay as long as we want!

I can totally picture us coming out of our quaint Scottish cottage, and riding to town on our vintage bicycles for tea. My bicycle would have a woven basket, probably filled with lavender or whatever grows in Scotland. Heather? Yes, filled with heather, and we'd bring bread to feed the ducks on the way into town. Or maybe they don't have ducks there. Sheep, then. We'd feed the sheep and then bicycle in to town for tea. With cream. And scones.

I don't get it. Why doesn't everyone homeschool?

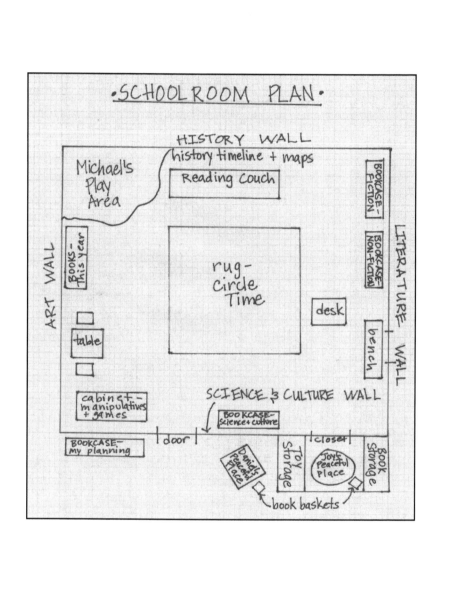

# ~ July ~

What a gorgeous afternoon—perfect for the sprinkler park on Riverside Drive. Cotton-ball clouds float overhead, and the Arkansas River sparkles happily along.

Michael is in a swim diaper (I forgot his swim trunks), sitting by the tiny fountains, trying to catch the glassy arcs of water as they bubble up from the ground. Daniel and Joy are playing with Vanessa's twins, all of them swinging like wet monkeys from the jungle gym.

Vanessa was my college roommate. She's in town for the day to help me in my quest to Become an Organized Person.

Not that I'm totally disorganized. I have some systems. Our clean laundry is sorted into pretty baskets in the laundry room, one for each person in the family. I have color-coded hooks hung in the garage for our coats. I purge the kids' rooms periodically and sort toys into plastic buckets that get rotated out.

The problem is—I'm outnumbered. My kids can make messes faster than I can clean. I feel like I keep getting farther and farther behind. The coloring sheets and artwork pile up, the bills need to be filed, and the car—well, let's not even talk about the car.

What I'm saying is: I've *got* to get organized this year and Vanessa's just the person to help me do it.

"I'm sort of compulsive about it," Vanessa said apologetically this morning in my kitchen.

"No, that's okay. I want to be compulsive too!" I earnestly told her. "Teach me how!"

Vanessa's home is very creative and colorful, but still clean. Simple. That's what I want. Not a lot of visual clutter clogging up my brain. Granted, Vanessa's twins are eight, and they go to school. And she doesn't have a toddler. But still, I figure I can learn some things.

Here are the three things she told me to work on:

1. **Routine.** John and I have to get in the habit of making our bed every day and picking up our room. (Okay, *I* have to get in the habit; it's usually my clothes strewn about.) Otherwise, how can I expect the kids to make their own beds and keep their rooms clean? This is a good point.

2. **Simplify.** I am supposed to clean out the kids' toys (again) and give, throw, or store away unnecessary stuff. (The question is when? Her kids are in school all day, and mine are here with me all day. I have to figure that part out.)

3. **Put things in their homes.** We are going to work on everything having a "home" and making sure we all put things in their homes. I have been letting the kids get away with leaving messes in their wakes, as if they were clothes- and shoe-spewing tornadoes.

I am going to turn the playroom into a schoolroom, and I'm sure it will help a lot, to have all our school stuff in one area instead of littered around the house. I've got the curriculum and other stuff from the convention arranged and ready to go.

I feel more organized already.

*****

After our hard work this morning, Vanessa and I decided that we all deserved a trip to the park. We went through the McDonald's drive-through and got the kids Happy Meals and ourselves salads.

Now Vanessa and I are at the sprinkler park under the shade of a tree, lazily watching the kids. Lazily, in the sense of being prepared at any moment to jump up and grab a baby who's tipped over and could drown, while simultaneously checking on the big kids to make sure they don't break an arm. That Mom kind of lazy.

I forgot how people always stare at Vanessa. She looks a lot like Gwyneth Paltrow with long blonde hair and blue eyes, but she is quiet and unassuming. In college, total strangers used to stop her on the sidewalk and ask her out. It was unbelievable. And a bit annoying.

The thing I love about Vanessa, though, is that she always seeks God's will for her life and doesn't worry about what other people think. She got her degree in Music Performance and went to Nashville after school but never made it big. A lot of people thought she was crazy for pursuing that ("Do you know how hard it is to make it big in Christian music?") but she felt like God gave her the gift of her voice, and it was what He was leading her to do at the time. So she went.

While she was in Nashville, she worked at a print shop to pay the bills and learned a lot. She has a great eye for design, so now she does graphic design work from home while her kids are at school. She is always using her creativity to serve others, doing projects for her church or different ministries just to help them out. I'm constantly amazed by the creativity and brilliance of my friends.

"We should get back," Vanessa says, checking her watch. We drove separately so that she could head straight back to her ranch in Northeastern Oklahoma as soon as we're finished.

"I know. We should go too. But they're so happy!" I hate to leave when everyone's content, and I am actually getting to have an adult conversation. I'm letting Joy and Michael skip their naps, but maybe they'll fall asleep in the car on the way home.

"We can stay a little bit longer." Vanessa stretches out in the shade and takes a sip of Coke. "I only have work waiting for me when I get back anyway."

"How's work going?" I ask.

"Oh, fine. Things have been a little slow with the economy. But, it's some extra money anyway, and I like doing something creative. What about you—do you think you'll ever go back to work? For money, I mean."

We both laugh. We hate it when people ask if we "work." We are mothers; what do they think?

"Honestly, I have no desire for a cubicle again." I shudder at the thought. "Or computer programming. That was *so* not me."

"Yeah, talk about a terrible career match for you, my creative, non-technical friend."

"I know," I smile. "Ridiculous. But, as hard as staying home is, as physically and emotionally exhausting as it is, it's a pretty great job. I get to make my own schedule, finger paint, and snuggle up and read books to my kids. I feel like I get to help my children be anchored in this world. It's so much more interesting than programming ever was."

"You don't get bored?"

"Well, there's still that strange mix of too much to do—like laundry and dishes—but somehow being bored to tears. Maybe it's the lack of other adults? But as the kids get older there's less of that. I can have actual conversations with Daniel and Joy now.

"But, you know?" I add, after thinking for a minute, "It's challenging too. In my old job I felt like I used one tiny part of my brain, and did the same thing over and over again. Now I feel like I'm getting to use more of my whole brain. And, yeah, it's hard, but I like a challenge. Technical work in an office was honestly much more boring for me."

We watch our children play together. Daniel and Vanessa's son are chasing each other in the grass, their bodies lithe and glistening, like dolphins in the sun. Vanessa's daughter and Joy are picking dandelions and blowing the seeds into the wind while Michael giggles and claps. They are all joy and awe and wonder.

"I mean, what could be more important and precious work?" I am careful because I don't want to offend Vanessa or seem like I think less of her for choosing to work and send her kids to school. I am just trying to explain. "I read this quote by Abigail Adams the other day about how if we are raising heroes, philosophers, and statesmen then we need learned women. That's us, right? What nobler work could we have than raising these precious little ones to love the Lord and follow Him with their lives? They're going to change the world someday."

"Oh, you're so right!" Vanessa breathes, her eyes filling with tears. "I pray for my children every day as they ride off on the bus. I pray for their safety, and that they would have an influence on the classmates, not the other way around. I want them to make a difference in the world."

"They will." I give her a hug. "They already do. You are an amazing, creative, godly mother, and your children will be just like you when they grow up. I can tell about these things."

We laugh, and we wipe away a few tears. What is it with talking about my children and the Lord? It makes me cry every time!

We silently watch the kids, golden and happy in the sun.

"It's scary though, isn't it?" Vanessa says softly. "I mean, what if we mess them up?"

"I know," I sigh. "Especially if you homeschool. Then you can't even blame a teacher! It's my job to teach them everything. It's a lot of responsibility, and it's sort of terrifying. It's all on my shoulders."

"It's not *all* on your shoulders," Vanessa says, and I know what she means.

\*\*\*\*\*

We stayed too long.

We let the kids have an ice cream (those darned music-playing ice cream trucks), then they had to go rinse off in the fountains again, and then Vanessa and I had to dry them off and get them in the cars. Vanessa and her kids are already gone.

Everyone is melting with exhaustion. Daniel complained and groaned all the way to the car; Michael is sticky and fussy; and Joy is having trouble obeying anything I'm telling her, which I know means she's having a Tired Crash.

Normally, with her pretty heart-shaped face, blonde hair, and sparkling brown eyes, Joy looks as if she could be sitting at a desk in a *Pottery Barn Kids* catalog. Right now though, her hair is wild and her face grimy; she looks like a bedraggled and potentially violent street urchin.

The problem is—I've *got* to run by Whole Foods on the way home. My sister got me hooked on these apple chips, and I need to get a few other things that the normal grocery store doesn't carry. Otherwise, we have to drive all the way across town tomorrow. I just need to pop in.

"Hey guys, want some fizzy juice?" I lay out the bait. "And a zucchini muffin?"

"A kiwi muffin?" Joy suddenly pays attention. "Yes! I *love* kiwi muffins!"

"*Zucch*ini muffin," Daniel mutters.

"Okay, then we need to quickly get in the car and pop in to Whole Foods," I say in my super-excited mom voice. "Then we'll go home and watch a movie." Nothing like bribery.

Only, I realize Joy is soaking wet. What did she do, run through the sprinkler after I dried her off? I can't take her into Whole Foods like this; she'll get a cold.

Aha! I have a stroke of brilliance. There's a Salvation Army right up the street! We can go there, see if we find any bargains, and get some dry clothes all at the same time. I feel like one of those quick-thinking moms on TV. I should be in a Mentos commercial.

I get them all buckled in, and we drive up the street to the Salvation Army. We walk in the store and back to the racks of children's clothes.

"I'm freezing!" Joy shivers and hugs herself to warm up.

"Okay, honey. We're going to change into dry clothes here in just a sec," I say, as I scan the rack. Yes! A flowery yellow Gap skirt—$2.99. Great. I grab it. And here's a pink T-shirt. Perfect.

"Joy, go put these on in the dressing room, please." I point Joy to the dressing room against the wall. She doesn't move.

"Mommy, I want this shirt." Joy has spotted a sparkly green spaghetti-strap tank top. Size four.

Really? What is wrong with people? Who would make a spaghetti-strap tummy-showing tank top for a little girl? And who would buy it?

"Joy, we're not getting that." My voice is firm. "It's not modest. We don't show our tummies."

"I want it." Joy's eyes have turned to stone. Her lips are in a thin line.

"Joy. We're not getting it. Here are your clothes. Please go put them on."

Clearly I can't give in. She's being ridiculous. She can't wear that shirt. Okay, forget about Whole Foods; we just need to get home. Joy's hit the wall. She's in the Land of the Irrational, as John and I call it. If we were at home I'd put her in Time Out or to bed. But I can't do that here, obviously.

"No." Joy stares at me defiantly. "I. Want. This. Shirt."

I've seen this look before. This child has a will of steel. When I make her sit at dinner until she eats three bites of whatever I've served (Three bites! That's it!), she often stays in her chair two *hours* and then falls asleep on the table. I do not have time to have a two-hour showdown at Salvation Army. I'm going to pay for this later, but I decide to compromise.

"All right," I say. "We can get it for your dress-up. But you can only wear it for dress-up, understand?" I'll throw it away next week when she's forgotten about it.

"Okay," Joy says with a glint in her eye. She knows she's won. That little stinker. Now I'm irritated at myself and her.

"Can I go put my new clothes on?" Joy whines. "I'm freezing."

"Yes, good idea." I pull the tags off the skirt and T-shirt, give her the clothes, and take her to the dressing room. It's only about fifteen steps away from the cashier, so I can keep my eyes on the dressing room door the whole time and pay for the clothes while she changes.

I take the tags and go to the cashier. Daniel is whining about going home, and Michael is starting to cry in the car seat. I know Daniel will flip out if I tell him that we aren't going to get fizzy juice and muffins after all, so I'll just keep that bit of information to myself for now.

"Thank you." I take our bag from the man checking us out, trying to seem calm and unruffled. I feel like a bit of a crazy person anyway for taking wet children into a store.

We go to get Joy from the dressing room, and I find her there, buck naked, making faces at herself in the mirror.

"Joy," I try to use a patient voice. "Why are your clothes not on?"

She makes a face at herself in the mirror. She crosses her arms and furrows her brow, making what I guess is Joy's Angry Face. We have got to get out of here. My heart begins to beat faster.

"Here, let me help you." I leave Daniel outside to keep an eye on Michael in his car seat and go into the room with Joy.

"NO! I. Will. Do it!" she says bossily.

"Okay," I say firmly. "You have three minutes to *put your clothes on*. Or I'm doing it for you." I close the door. I am starting to sweat.

"It's okay, sweetie," I tell Michael who is fussing and acting hungry. I have goldfish out in the car, but we've got to *get* to the car first. I take him out of the car seat, so I can hold him and comfort him.

After about two minutes, I knock on the door.

"Joy?" No answer. I open the door.

Joy is sitting, still completely naked, on the bench, looking at herself in the mirror. She sticks out her tongue at herself, then laughs.

Okay, now I'm mad. This is ridiculous. She's totally ignoring me. This child…

Stay calm. I have got to get this girl to the car. If she's not going to dress herself, I have to do it for her. I warned her.

"Daniel, watch Michael for me, okay?" I say to him, and sit Michael on the floor. Thank heavens Daniel is obeying. "You're doing a good job helping Mommy. Thank you." I kiss him on the head and go into the dressing room.

"Here, Mommy's just going to put your shirt on, okay, honey?" I am trying to not anger the beast.

I pop her shirt over her head, then put one arm through. Suddenly she realizes what I'm doing.

"NO!" she screams. "I *said*, I was going to *do it*!" She has gone over to the dark side.

"No," I say in a low tone, trying to keep our voices down. These walls are paper thin. "You didn't obey, so Mommy has to do it now. It's okay."

"NOOOOOOOO!" she screams. She pulls her arm out of the sleeve and wriggles out of the shirt.

We hardly ever spank, but I really wish I could right now. There's no way I'm doing that in public though; they'd probably call the police on me.

I hear Michael starting to wail outside the door. My heart is starting to pound.

"Mom!" Daniel is saying in his panicky voice. "Michael's crying! He needs you!"

We have got to get out of here. I am going to have to wrestle this child into her clothes. I hold her down and put the shirt over her head and arms.

"OWWWW! Mommy you're hurting me!" she screams.

"It wouldn't hurt if you would stop fighting me!" I hiss at her. "Stop. Calm down."

I try to sit and hold her for a minute to calm her down, but she sees herself in the mirror and gets inspired again. Now she's putting on a show. She makes an angry face at herself and then turns back to me.

This is completely ridiculous. I stuff her legs into the skirt. We're almost there. I can just scoop her up and leave. Forget underwear.

"OWWWW! Mommy!!! Stop!!!!" she's shrieking at the top of her lungs.

I hear a knock on the door.

"Yes?" I reply.

"What's going on in there?" asks a woman in a threatening voice.

"What?" I say, annoyed. I open the door a crack and see a young lady, maybe in her twenties. This lady doesn't even work here. She's just another shopper. What is she doing? Who does she think she is, butting into this? Meanwhile, Joy has wriggled out of the shirt and skirt again, and stands naked with her arms crossed across her chest glaring at me.

"Is there a *problem*?" the woman says imperiously.

"Yes, there's a *problem*." I fling open the door so she can see Joy who is shocked into silence. "I'm trying to get my naked, screaming child dressed. Do you mind?"

"Well," says the woman in a haughty voice, "*I* believe parents are supposed to be *responsible* for their children's actions."

What is that supposed to mean? Does she see anyone else trying to be responsible for my children's actions? Who's in here trying to get her dressed? What does she expect me to be doing—I have a baby and another kid here. I would be happy to leave if I could.

Then it hits me what to say.

"Oh, *great!*" I say in a fake delighted voice, "Are you offering to help? *Fabulous!*"

The other shoppers are staring at the scene by now, and this lady is trapped. Ha!

"All right, I can help," the lady says grudgingly.

"*Won*derful!" I say in a saccharine voice with a big smile. "You can carry my car seat. Daniel, you carry Michael. And I'll carry my naked, screaming child! *Thanks!*"

My face burning with embarrassment, I wrap up Joy the best I can in the clothes and, holding my head high, walk through the crowd of staring people to the car. I buckle Joy in, still naked, but finally silenced. I pile the clothes on top of her as best I can. I take the car seat from the lady.

"Thanks *so* much! I *really* appreciate it!" I tell her with a huge, fake smile. She stomps off in a huff, annoyed that she ended up helping me instead of finishing her speech, I guess.

I buckle Michael in, give him some goldfish, and help Daniel into the back. We drive home. Joy has resumed crying and screaming at the top of her lungs. Michael is whimpering. Daniel is sitting in stunned silence.

This is, officially, the Worst Parenting Moment of My Life.

And, it was all my fault. I know better than this. Why did I take hot, tired, cranky children into a store? What is wrong with me?

My mind flashes back to how brilliant I thought I was with that great idea. Talk about pride going before a fall.

My cheeks are still flushed with humiliation. I'm annoyed at myself for setting my daughter up for that one. I'm embarrassed for how my daughter (and I) just acted. I'm angry with that lady for treating me like I'm abusing my children.

A thought hits me—if I can't even get Joy to put her clothes on, how am I ever going to teach her to read this year? Maybe it's crazy to think I can homeschool Daniel and Joy and deal with a baby. Maybe Joy would do better with someone else teaching her. Maybe Vicky is right; maybe I am going to ruin their lives.

Suddenly I remember our trip to California. We've decided to go, but John has a business trip in Chicago the week before, so the plan was for him to meet us there. Which means I will be flying with the three kids by myself. I thought I could handle it. I am beginning to have doubts.

This meltdown was horrible, but at least it was brief. What if that happens on the plane?

As Joy's wailing begins to subside in the backseat, I silently pray.

*Lord, help me.*

# Plane Backpack Packing List

CODE GREEN (everyone happy)
- Snacks: almonds, raisins, granola bars
- New coloring books, crayons , Color Wonder markers
- Lift-the-flap books (Michael)
- Nursing cover
- Balloon - to blow up and deflate to amuse Michael

CODE YELLOW (people whining a bit)
- New drawing boards
- New sticker books (Dora/Star Wars)
- Puppets
- Lacing cards

CODE ORANGE (people whining a lot)
- DVD player (battery runs out in 1 hour; use wisely)
- DVDs - Praise Baby, Diego, Backyardigans

CODE RED (Must avert meltdown! )
- Gum
- Chocolate chip cookies
- Candy (as much as they want)
- John's iPod (they'll fight over it, so use only in emergency)

Julianne Miller

# ~ August ~

Even though it's technically a vacation, I consider this trip to California to be the beginning of our school year. It feels like my first homeschool test, and it consists of three questions:

1. Can I control my children well enough without John's help that we survive the flight meltdown-free?
2. Will Daniel and Joy learn anything?
3. Will I return home with my sanity intact?

We board the plane for the first flight. Since there are only three seats per row, and Michael has to have his own seat, Daniel has to sit by himself on a different row. This is slightly terrifying to me.

I nurse Michael during takeoff, and he doesn't cry at all. I am using my nursing cover, wearing a jacket (for maximum coverage), and Joy is in the seat next to me as a buffer, so it's not too awkward. Much better than having to sit by a poor, unsuspecting male stranger while I nurse.

We work through our backpack full of activities, and everyone does great; Daniel acts like a tiny grown-up the whole time. I am so proud of him!

Now, on the second flight, Joy wants to be the one to sit by herself. I let her, against my better judgment. She is doing wonderfully too! I am shocked. I think part of it is that Daniel and Joy feel like such big kids when they get to sit by themselves, and part is that I explained they have to help Mommy, or we won't make it to California. And part might be that I am praying without ceasing.

I think another reason Joy is doing so well on this flight is that we did an Obedience Boot Camp the week before we left. The kids go through these phases where they think they are in charge, and we have to crack down on every little thing. It's a tiring week, but their behavior is much better afterwards.

Joy had been throwing tantrums whenever she didn't get her way, especially in public. The Salvation Army episode was the worst one, but there were others. I knew she had to realize that if she threw a tantrum in public, we would stop everything until she calmed down. She had to know Mommy would outlast her. So John and I set her up.

We took the kids to Target on a Saturday morning, knowing Joy would test us about something. She did; she demanded jelly beans, and we had the nerve to refuse. I carried her, kicking and screaming, out to the lawn beside the building. I said, "When you choose to calm down, we'll go back inside." I held her firmly while she cried, "Daddy! I want Daddy!" (I got lots of sympathetic smiles from other moms who walked by.) After about fifteen minutes, she decided to calm down. We talked about how she didn't get to do fun things if she couldn't obey. She apologized; we hugged and prayed, and she's been much better ever since. She seems to need a periodic reminder that she's not actually in charge of the family.

As the plane touches down in Orange County, I breathe a sigh of relief. (John says I'm a pessimist about flights, but I have reason to be. I call it being a realist. And a mom.) John is waiting for us at the baggage carousel—his flight got in earlier. Dave, Ginger and their kids are coming tomorrow.

John loads the bags in the rental car, and we drive to the hotel as evening settles, purple and misty, on the coast. We approach the impressive stone-columned portico and pull into the valet line.

A polished lady in a chic black suit approaches our car. "Welcome to the St. Regis. Are you checking in or just here for the wedding this evening?"

"Checking in," John says.

"Okay. Valet parking is thirty dollars per day, and we'll be happy to help you with your bags. Here's your ticket for the dashboard…"

"How much is it if we just park it ourselves?" John asks.

"Well, self-park is twenty-four dollars a day, but unfortunately, it's full at the moment. We have seven hundred guests arriving for a reception."

"All right, thank you," John smiles. He is not one to argue. As we pull up to the legion of waiting valets, we discuss how ridiculous it is that the hotel charges us for valet parking when there is no other option.

"At least you can expense it," I remind John.

"I know," he sighs, "but it's the principle of it! You know, that principle of not having to pay outrageous sums of money for things you can do perfectly well yourself?" I agree with him on this one.

We follow the BMWs, Lexuses, and some so-fancy-I-don't-even-know-what-they-are cars up the flagstone drive. The license plate in front of us reads: CONSUL. From all the gorgeous women in sparkly saris milling about, I am guessing that this reception is for a family member of the Indian or Pakistani consulate.

We struggle to get our bags onto the bellman's cart and into the palatial lobby where impeccably dressed men and women stream past. I try to keep Daniel from crashing into one stunning woman with long, glossy blonde hair. The heels of her Christian Louboutin shoes tap smartly on the marble floor as she glides by us in her tight, black dress. (I only know the brand because her shoes have red soles. All I know is red soles equals expensive. And, is there some kind of patent on that?

Why aren't there red-soled knock-offs at Target? I don't know.) To put it mildly, these are not our kind of people.

I am wearing jeans and Crocs. I stand beside the bellhop's cart as John checks us in. We have four black bags, a 101 Dalmatians backpack, another backpack with all the plane diversions, two booster seats, one baby car seat, and two teddy bears.

I am pushing our dilapidated Graco stroller. The sunshade is tied onto it with string. (The stroller embarrasses John but I like it. We bought a new, much better-looking stroller, but it didn't work as well. This one is functional.)

I feel completely underdressed and conspicuous. I'm praying that the kids keep quiet and that we get to our room quickly.

The thing about small children is—there is such tremendous potential for disaster. They can poop, throw up, have a temper tantrum, run into people, and break things with no malice and virtually no warning. The best thing, I've learned, is to *stay as far away from polite society as possible.*

We follow the bellhop through the lobby and past a room with expensive-looking vases in alcoves. We pass a study where a businessman is working on his laptop in a sumptuous chair by a roaring fire. Daniel has no inside voice, so I'm constantly shushing him. How hard is it to remember not to yell EVERY WORD? Very hard, apparently.

I have to keep reminding him of things that don't seem that difficult to remember like, "Don't run, and stop flinging yourself into walls." These are things grown-ups don't do. Have I ever thought, "Hey, I know—I'll start running full-tilt and go smack myself into the wall so I can say 'Ooof!' and ooze to the floor in mock pain?" No, no I have not.

We go past the coffee shop, the gift shop, and marble spiral staircase. The spa is to the right. We turn left and wind past the huge windows that overlook the terraced gardens, fountains, and pools. The bellhop leads us to the elevator, and then down long hallways, until we finally arrive at our room.

We straggle into our room, and John tips the bellhop. I collapse on the bed while the kids run happily in circles. This would be fine if everything weren't so...*white*. The bed linens are ivory; the throw pillows are snowy white. The chairs and footstools are covered in a creamy suede, and the carpet is light beige. Do rich people not spill things?

At fourteen months Michael has just started walking and John and I have nicknamed him the BMD, Baby of Mass Destruction, for good reason. He has already climbed onto the chair, then onto the desk, grabbed the phone receiver, and he starts slamming it down on the phone.

"Michael, no bang!" John says firmly.

Michael looks at him with his sparkly, brown baby eyes, laughs, and whacks the receiver again onto the desk.

John goes over and lifts Michael down, only to have him toddle over to the window and start yanking at the blinds. Finally, John gets a ball out of the backpack to keep Michael happy for a few minutes.

"Guys, calm down," I say nervously, as Daniel and Joy shriek and tumble over things. "And see this little fridge? Don't get anything out of here, okay?"

"Awesome!" Daniel eyes the candy bars and cans of pop in the mini-bar fridge. "They left us Snickers!"

"Yes, that Snickers costs...let's see." John scans the price list. "Eight dollars. It's about fifty cents at the grocery store."

"Eight *dollars*?" Daniel's eyes widen in shock.

"Eight *dollars*?" Joy shrieks, imitating Daniel's look of horror. She has no idea how much eight dollars is. It could be eight hundred for all she knows. She's still trying to figure out the difference between a quarter and zoo money.

"Yes," John says in a serious tone. "So don't touch any of this, okay? Not even a bottle of water. Okay?"

"But what if we're so thirsty we're about to *die*?" Daniel begins to panic. He's extremely talented at scaring himself.

"You're not going to die." John looks exasperated. "And if you're thirsty, you can ask us for a drink of water from the sink."

I peek into the bathroom, which is its own separate suite complete with live orchids, a Jacuzzi tub, and white fluffy towels. I notice that there are no plastic water cups, only fragile-looking glasses that look disturbingly like crystal.

There are so very many things for us to break or ruin here. Luxury stresses me out.

*****

It's Monday morning. For the last three days, the kids have been waking up at 4:30 a.m. — their normal hour if it weren't for that pesky time change. Today, John and I have kept them quiet in the hotel room for as long as possible: we've eaten granola bars, read *The Princess and the Kiss,* and watched *Backyardigans — The Legend of the Volcano Sisters.* It's now 6:30 a.m., John is getting ready for a business breakfast, and I'm out of tricks. It's raining outside. I think I might splurge on the hotel buffet breakfast, so we don't have to drive anywhere. I pick up the phone and press zero to reach the front desk.

"Hello," I greet the man who answers. "Can you tell me the cost of your breakfast buffet, please?"

"Eighty dollars, ma'am."

"I'm sorry, eigh*teen* dollars?" I ask.

"Eight-tee. Actually $79.95."

"For one person?"

"Yes, ma'am."

"O-kay! Thank you very much!" I say brightly and hang up. What are they serving, caviar and diamonds with their eggs? I decide that we'll go to Chick-fil-A.

We leave our room and head to the elevators. Daniel pushes Michael in the stroller; Joy clomps merrily along in her red-sequined dress-up shoes. What was I thinking when I said she could bring those on the trip?

I shush the kids all the way down the long hallway, past rooms full of sleeping people, then corral them into the elevator. I take a deep breath and close my eyes, resting my head against the wall.

"No!" Joy screams. "Michael, don't push that!" My eyes fly open to see Michael leaning forward in his stroller to jab the elevator's red alarm button.

"Michael, stop." I roll the stroller back away from the buttons, and the buzzing stops. I smile, thinking of how five years ago I probably would have freaked out if my child pushed the alarm button. I have since learned that kids will push buttons, alarms will buzz and then stop, and life will go on.

This elevator seems to be different though. As we reach the ground floor and step off, I hear a recorded voice saying something about the alarm. Boy, these fancy hotels really go over the top about everything.

We walk down the hall and pass a hotel employee. He looks at us with an odd look, but it's not surprising. I'm sure we look a bit more bedraggled than their typical hotel guests.

We continue into the lobby and past the concierge desk. "Sorry if you heard that elevator alarm," I say to the morning concierge. "My baby pushed the button." I laugh and give her an apologetic shrug.

"What?" she says, her face turning pale. "Your baby pushed the alarm button?"

"Um, yes." I'm getting a strange feeling in my stomach.

"But the person came on and you told them it wasn't an emergency, right?"

"Person?" I say weakly.

"Yes; the alarm button is directly connected to the fire department. If you don't respond and tell them that it's not an emergency, they send a fire truck."

"A fire truck?" Daniel's eyes light up. "Cool!"

"Shhh," I hiss to Daniel. "Oh my," I tell the concierge. "I am so sorry. I thought it was a recording."

"That's okay," she says with a tight-lipped smile. "We'll take care of it."

"Is there anything I can do?" I say, feeling my face flush hot.

"No, we'll handle it." She tries to look as though she doesn't want to kill me but doesn't quite succeed. She hurries over to the front desk to whisper to the two men on duty. They look over at us. One man grabs the phone and starts punching the buttons.

Okay, I think the best solution is to vacate the premises immediately. "I'm so sorry," I tell them, with a cringing smile, as we quickly head outside. So much for flying under the radar.

I keep shushing Joy and Daniel while we wait for the valet to get our car. They are excitedly pummeling me with questions: "What happened? What's going on? Is a fire truck coming?" For the love of all that is good, would you please be quiet?

I try to appear nonchalant in front of the other valets when I hear the wailing siren in the distance. It's amazing how many blasted people they have working so early in the morning. I try to act casual. Fire truck, hmm, how interesting. Wonder what that's all about?

After what seems like eighteen years, the valet arrives, and I hurry the kids inside the car. I drive down the palm-tree-lined driveway, past the enormous fountain and beautifully manicured gardens, and out onto the road just as the fire truck comes through the front gate.

*****

Blessedly, we make it to Chick-fil-A without further incident. It's now seven o'clock in the morning, and I'm ready for a nap. The kids eat chicken nuggets (yes, they serve them for breakfast), and I order an egg and chicken bagel. I sit by the window and watch the rain pound the sidewalk while I sip hot tea; the kids tumble around the empty play area. They are much safer there, away from pristine hotel rooms and nowhere near elevator buttons.

I'm trying to figure out what we're going to do today. The beach may be out. John and Dave have conference sessions all day; Ginger and her kids are probably still asleep.

The last two days have been damp and gray, but we managed to do what we had planned. Saturday we visited the San Juan Capistrano Mission, a beautiful, though remarkably one-sided, representation of the Spanish Mission era in California. Yesterday John braved the weather and took the kids out to the chilly pool. They lasted about fifteen minutes, then came in shivering. I thought this was sunny southern California; it seems more like Seattle to me.

I was so excited about going to the beach; it is a ten-hour drive from Tulsa to the nearest ocean. I was hoping the kids could build sandcastles, collect shells, and play in the waves.

"How often is the weather like this?" I ask the girl who is wiping off tables at Chick-fil-A.

"Never!" she said. "I'm from Kansas, and we had big thunderstorms all the time *there*. It *never* does this *here*!"

I smile at her, but as I look out the window to see the lightning streak through the ominous clouds, followed by the sound of booming thunder, I can't help but think, in a *Princess Bride* moment: I don't think that word 'never' means what you think it means.

My phone rings. I look at the display and see the caller's name. "Hey, Ginger," I answer.

"Hey, Julianne," Ginger says morosely. "What are you guys doing?"

"We're at Chick-fil-A. I'm thinking about going to a children's museum in Irvine if this doesn't clear up soon." I think the museum is geared for younger kids, so I don't even suggest it to her. "Are you guys still going to Disneyland?"

"No way." Ginger is not one for braving the elements. "We might go to Downtown Disney, because at least we can be inside the shops. Or I might get a babysitter from the hotel and go to the spa."

I can hear Drew in the background saying, "I want to go to Disney! Mom, you *promised!*"

"Drew, I'm sorry. We can't go today. It's pouring down rain. We'll try tomorrow, okay?"

I hear Maddie whining, "Mom, this is so *boring*. What are we going to do?"

"I gotta go," Ginger says tersely.

"All right." I can sympathize. "We'll see you later." I'm still holding out for sun. Meanwhile, I decide to have the kids do some school.

I go into the play area with our backpack and colored pencils. Michael has a ball (I take one everywhere we go), and he's rolling it up the slide and catching it. He thinks this is quite entertaining.

Before we left on the trip, we read two easy reader books: *Dust for Dinner*, about people heading west to California during the Dust Bowl, and *Listening to Whales Sing*, since we hope to see whales.

On the trip, I want the kids to do a journal page for each day. Just a picture of something and one or two sentences.

"Okay, guys, come over here. We're going to do a journal page," I announce.

"We're playing Eggs Crackin' Out! Can't we finish?" Daniel begs. Eggs Crackin' Out is a game of their own invention in which they curl up in balls and pretend to be baby dinosaurs hatching. Usually they rope me in, and I have to be the mother dinosaur and feed them leaves and worms.

"No, let's do our journals first, then you can finish playing." I use my best firm but sweet mommy voice.

"Yay!" Joy says happily. Usually if an activity involves colored pencils, she's in.

"Awww!" Daniel whines.

"Daniel, please don't complain. Let's just do it, and you'll be done." Honestly, does he not understand that most kids have to go to school for six hours a day? It's one little journal page. "Just draw a picture of the dolphin cruise yesterday and write one sentence."

"One sentence?" Daniel begins to panic. "I can't write a sentence!"

"Okay, tell me what you want to say and I'll write it down and you copy it." I am trying to be understanding. Handwriting is our most painful subject. Daniel can do fine, but he thinks he can't, and he gets frustrated because he can't write the letters perfectly. He doesn't like writing a sentence because he's afraid he'll spell something wrong.

"Why don't you start with the picture?" I suggest. "I'll help Joy while you draw."

"Whew," Daniel sighs, as though he's narrowly escaped having to walk the plank. He starts to work on his picture.

John's conference didn't start until last night, so yesterday morning the whole family went on a dolphin cruise through The Ocean Institute, a hands-on aquarium with the motto: "Experience is the Teacher." Out on the water, the instructors led a science lab to study mud from the bottom of the sea floor and see what tiny organisms they could find. Then the boat caught up with a pod of hundreds of dolphins. The water was suddenly alive with gleaming, silvery arcs, filling the waves with beauty. The dolphins raced next to the ship in playful, undulating streaks, as if they wanted the kids to jump in and join them. Daniel and Joy shrieked with excitement: "Daddy! There's one!"and, "Mommy, look at them all!" I want them to write a journal entry about it so they really remember the whole experience.

"Joy, what do you want to say about the dolphin cruise?" I have my pencil ready to write as she dictates.

"I would like to say…" Joy says spinning around in a circle, "… that there was this huge thing you put your eyes in to see far away. Daddy lifted me up to see. Then, next to the boat, there were these big, huge dolphins! We were waiting for the humpback whales but they didn't show up. And then we had hot chocolate!"

"Wow, Joy, that is so good!" I finish writing down her words. "Can you draw a picture to go with your story?"

"Sure!" Joy chirps and starts to draw.

"Okay, Daniel, can I see your picture?" I turn to see Daniel's journal. Michael has commandeered a colored pencil, so I give him a blank page to scribble on.

"It's terrible," Daniel says morosely.

"It's not terrible!" I encourage him. He's drawn waves and a boat, with dolphin fins in the water and rocks off to the side. "It's a good picture."

"I hate it," he groans. "I'll never be able to do it!" He puts his head down on the floor.

It's hard to tell how much of his whining is because he doesn't want to do the work and how much is genuine insecurity. Either way, he needs to do it.

"Daniel, that's not true and it's not helpful." I try to be patient. "You *can* do it. It just takes work. I'll help you, and we'll do it together. What do you want to say about it?"

"I don't know," Daniel moans into the floor.

"Anything. You can tell me about the dolphins, or the boat, or the weather, or what you liked best, or the hot chocolate. Anything you want."

"Can I just do one sentence?"

"Yes. One sentence is fine."

"Any sentence?"

"Any sentence."

Daniel pauses for a minute. "Is, 'It was good.' a sentence?"

I try not to sigh. "Yes. That's a sentence. That's what you want to say?"

"Yes," decides Daniel. "'It was good.'"

"Fine." I write it down. He can do better than this. But I'm not going to push him on it today. I did tell him any sentence.

Michael is getting tired of scribbling and starts throwing the pencils across the play area.

"Michael, no throw!" I tell him firmly. He grins at me and lobs another pencil across the room.

Sigh. I go scoop up Michael, ignoring his screams of protest. We need to wrap this up.

"Okay, Daniel, finish up. We need to go." I am thinking we better give up on the beach and go to the children's museum today. It's still pouring.

"I can't write this!" Daniel is moaning.

Oh, for heaven's sake. This should take five minutes, and we've been doing it for thirty. *Patience, Lord, give me patience.*

"Why not? Why can't you write it?" I ask, trying to be calm.

"Because my writing is terrible!" He furiously erases the word "It."

"It doesn't have to be perfect, Daniel; just do your best, okay?"

"No, it's my journal. I want it to be good."

How can I argue with that? "Well, you finish up, and I'm going to wait out here. Whenever you're done you can play Eggs

Crackin' Out for fifteen more minutes, and then we're going to go. So, the faster you finish, the faster you can play, all right?"

"All right," Daniel says, still looking depressed. I take Michael out of the play area back to the table and strap him into his high chair. He is crying now, mad that he had to leave the play area. I give him a hash brown and some chocolate milk to cheer him up.

I sit, sipping my tea and staring into the gray morning. I really wanted the kids to do a journal page every day, but this is excruciating. Should it be this hard? Maybe Daniel is not developmentally ready for this yet. Should I force him to do his journal and use every last shred of patience I have? Or should I give up on the writing and try again in a few months? I don't know.

I don't remember any of my homeschool books covering whining and groaning to this extent. Maybe I should look again.

*****

The children's museum is great—Michael digs in the pretend garden for plastic potatoes, Joy velcroes apples and oranges to trees and plays in the miniature house, and Daniel builds things with boards.

As I'm driving back to the hotel, Ginger calls to invite us to dinner with their family at the hotel's oceanfront restaurant, but I tell her I'm not up for that. Too much potential for disaster— once a day is enough. She gets quite a kick out of my fire truck story, though. I decide to go through the El Pollo Loco drive-thru and get chicken and tortillas for our family's dinner.

Now we are back at the hotel, and the sun is finally peeking through the clouds. John is out of his conference for the day, so we decide to take our dinner down to the beach for a picnic. We're not sure how many chances we will get this week.

The shuttle picks us up from the patio. The shuttle is basically a golf cart with no seat belts and open sides; it seems to me the ideal vehicle for plunging down the hill to our deaths. I hang onto Michael, and John clutches Daniel and Joy as the driver careens cheerily down the hill, around curves, and screeches to a halt at the entrance to the beach. We disembark and stagger down the ramp to the beach.

I round the corner and catch my breath. The view is amazing. The resort's private beach is deserted; the only sounds are the waves crashing rhythmically on the shore and seagulls squawking overhead. The fiery sun melts into the water, leaving the heavens streaked with amethyst. Daniel and Joy kick off their shoes and gleefully start filling their complimentary hotel buckets with sand. Michael seems scared of the sand and clings to me with his soft arms tight around my neck.

"It's okay, Buddy," I tell him. "Sand! See, it's okay."

"Sah," Michael repeats.

"Right, Buddy! It's sand! See?"

I let Michael feel the sand with his hands and feet, but he doesn't seem to trust it. The most sand he's ever seen is in the sandbox at the park. He is content to sit on my lap, watching the waves and seagulls with delight.

Behind us on the cliff, soft light glows from the windows of the exclusive restaurant in which Dave and Ginger are dining. I have no desire to trade places with them. The true riches are out here. They may be enjoying a fine meal, but they aren't feeling the sand on their feet or the ocean air on their faces; they might be listening to lovely classical music, but how can it compare to the music of the waves and gulls? And I have the added bonus of a baby on my lap and chubby arms around my neck.

If I teach my children nothing else, I want to teach them to recognize true treasures—not jewels or palatial mansions, but this amazing world God created, the precious people around us, and His eternal Truth. For where my children's treasures are, there their hearts will also be.

We eat, then stay until it is dark, soaking up every perfect moment. Joy runs up and down the beach, collecting sea shells and chasing birds. John helps Daniel dig an enormous hole.

This is why I wanted to come to the beach. Who needs Disneyland when you can dig a hole in the sand with a stick? The kids are utterly content and at peace. They have freedom to run, to yell, to tumble around. They can work—making castles, collecting shells, finding treasures. They don't need or want "entertainment." Real life works fine, thank you very much.

This is how I want to raise them and one of the reasons I want to homeschool. I want them to get to explore the world, marvel at God's Creation, be awed by His power rolling in on the waves and breathless at His beauty hanging in the clouds. Not that they couldn't do that if they were in school—I guess I just want to be there for it. I want to be there with them as they discover this world, not only on vacation and in the summer, but in the quiet of ordinary days.

Soon everyone relinquishes their projects to the dark and comes to snuggle with me and Michael on our sandy towel. Our family sits, as darkness falls around us, breathing in the night and the salty spray, wanting to stay there forever. We are awed by the enormity of the ocean and the beach. I feel like we are each a grain of sand: part of the big picture, but not the center.

"Family Song," I whisper. Each month John picks a hymn, and we learn at least the first verse and sing it together before bed.

Tonight the words are fitting. John starts deep, and we join in. The kids draw close, and we hug them tight, looking out at the waves and praising the One who made them.

*O LORD my God! When I in awesome wonder*
*Consider all the works Thy hand hath made;*
*I see the stars, I hear the mighty thunder,*
*Thy pow'r throughout the universe displayed:*

*Then sings my soul, my Saviour God, to Thee,*
*How great Thou art! How great Thou art!*
*Then sings my soul, my Saviour God, to Thee,*
*How great Thou art! How great Thou art!*

| | Julianne | Daniel | Joy | Michael |
|---|---|---|---|---|
| | | | 2010/2011 School Schedule | |

| | Julianne | Daniel | Joy | Michael |
|---|---|---|---|---|
| 6:00 | Up, exercise | Sleep | Sleep | Sleep |
| 7:00 | Shower, get ready | Sleep | Sleep | Sleep |
| 7:30 | Breakfast, Quiet Time | Sleep | Sleep | Sleep |
| 8:00 | Make Breakfast | Breakfast/Bible | Breakfast/Bible | Nurse, Breakfast |
| 8:30 | Morning Chores | Morning Chores | Morning Chores | Morning Chores |
| **SCHOOL (upstairs in schoolroom)** | | | | |
| 9:00-9:20 | Opening Routine | Opening Routine | Opening Routine | Opening Routine |
| 9:20-9:40 | Joy's reading lesson | Play with Michael | Reading Lesson | Play with Daniel |
| 9:40-10:00 | Daniel's spelling lesson | Spelling Lesson | Play with Michael | Play with Joy |
| 10:00-10:20 | Circle Time | Circle Time | Circle Time | Circle Time |
| 10:20-10:40 | Math Time | Math | Math | With Julianne |
| 10:40-11:00 | Get ready for walk | Potty, shoes, coats, etc | | |
| 11:00-11:20 | Walk & Snack | Walk & Snack | | |
| 11:20-11:40 | Put Michael down | Journal Time | Journal Time | Nap |
| 11:40-12:00 | Help with Journals | Journal Time | Journal Time | Nap |
| 12:00-12:20 | Reading Time | Snuggle reading on couch w/Mom | | Nap |
| 12:20-12:40 | Chapter Book | Color while Mom reads | | Nap |
| 12:40-1:00 | Clean up & stickers | | | Nap |
| **LUNCH** | | | | |
| 1:00-2:00 | Lunch outside | | | |
| 2:00-3:00 | Play with Michael | Rest—alone | Rest—alone | Play with Mom |
| 3:00 | Housework | Curious George / Sid | Curious George/Sid | Help Mom |
| 4:00 | Play outside | Play outside | | |
| 5:00 | Get dinner ready | Play outside | Play outside | With Mom |
| 5:30 | Eat dinner | Dinner | | |
| 6:00 | Clean up | Ten-minute tidy – pick up toys | | |
| 6:30 | Break | John home – Daddy time | | |
| 7:30 | Toothbrush Time | Brush teeth, get ready for bed, nurse Michael | | |
| 8:00 | Reading/Bed | Reading, pray | | |
| 8:30 | Check email | Lights out | | |
| 9:00 | Bed | Sleep | | |

# ~ September ~

Today is our first official day of school.

The schoolroom has been ready since late July, and I've been dying to get up here and start school. It's so clean, everything bright and cheerful and inspiring.

When I walk in the door, I'm facing the red wall—the history and geography wall. There is a big map of the U.S. on one side and a giant world map on the other. In between is the couch where we will do our snuggle reading. Above the couch is our history timeline with a few pictures already up: George Washington, Laura Ingalls Wilder, and men and women from the Bible. Also against that wall is a gated-off play area with toys and blocks for Michael.

To the right is the blue wall—the literature wall. There are two tall bookcases—one for fiction books and the other for non-fiction. I didn't realize we had so many books! I even gave a lot away as I cleaned, and the bookcases are still almost full. There is a window on that wall with a wooden toy box in front of it that we'll use for a reading bench. A quaint refinished antique desk stands in front of the bookcases, giving the room that *Little House on the Prairie* feel.

The back wall is the science and culture wall. There's another bookcase with two high shelves. One shelf holds Creation treasures: birds' nests, robins' eggs, shells, and feathers. The other shelf has objects from our missionary friends around the world: wooden shoes from Holland, carved wood and beads from Africa, Navajo sand paintings from Arizona, and statues from Estonia. Also on this bookcase are the baskets that hold this year's workbooks and journals.

The fourth wall is our art wall. It is painted a bright buttercup yellow. I've hung ropes in lines and attached clothespins, so I can pin up the children's best artwork. Above that are four clipboards for the Artist and Poet of the Month studies. This month I've hung up a Mary Cassatt picture, *Children Playing at the Beach,* and the Robert Louis Stevenson poem "At the Sea-Side." We're going to continue the ocean theme from California. There's also a cabinet with doors for math manipulatives and games.

On the end of the art wall is yet another bookcase for this year's studies. One shelf is for chapter books like *Charlie and the Chocolate Factory, Mr. Popper's Penguins, The Hundred Dresses, Farmer Boy,* and an illustrated *Swiss Family Robinson.* The next shelf down is for picture books: fairy tales and fables, poetry, an illustrated *Pilgrim's Progress,* and books about America. The next shelf is for Daniel's readers (ones he can read by himself): *Henry and Mudge; Amelia Bedelia; Greg's Microscope; Keep the Lights Burning, Abbie; Roxaboxen;* and more. The next shelf is for Joy's books: some *Bob* books to use during her reading lessons, and others with simple vocabulary. The last shelf holds lift-the-flap and board books for Michael.

Daniel and Joy each have a Peaceful Place where they can go to read. I ran out of space in the schoolroom, plus I thought they might need to go somewhere quiet, so Daniel's Peaceful Place is a small chair in the hallway. Joy's is in the cleaned-out closet—I attached floaty, sparkly fabric to a hula-hoop and hung it from a hook on the ceiling, so she has a sheer fairyland for her Peaceful Place.

I've got our whole schedule typed out and taped to the door, and we're ready to begin. (I know Lisa told me to stick to the basics and only do three twenty-minute sessions a day, but there are so many things I want to fit in that I couldn't help myself.)

I ding the little silver teacher's bell that I got at the teacher supply store. "Ring, ring, ring the bell; I'm glad that you are here! Ring, ring, ring the bell; we know that God is near." This is the song I sing for the two-year-olds in Baby Bible at church, but even Daniel and Joy love it. They beam when I take the bell over to them to ding. Michael wants to keep dinging, however, and starts crying when I take it away.

"Okay, guys, go sit down on the polka-dot rug, please." In the middle of the room is a large, colorful rug with bright polka dots on it. Daniel and Joy go sit down. Michael runs around the room screaming "Aahhh! Aahhh!"

"Michael, can you go sit down? Sit on the polka-dot rug, buddy!" I coax him.

"I'll get him, Mom." Daniel gets up, picks up Michael, and carries him over to the rug. Michael starts to scream in protest.

"Michael, you have to sit down. Sit down, buddy!" Daniel has the sweetest voice when he talks to his little brother. He's going to be a good Daddy someday. Michael gets up and runs off the rug and over to his push toy in the corner.

"That's okay; let him go," I tell the kids. "We'll do this part without him." I lead them in "This is the Day the Lord Has Made," the Pledge of Allegiance, and some learning stretches. I had read about how stretching improves blood flow to the brain and wakes up their minds and bodies, so I decided to try it. Daniel cannot manage to stay on the rug though; he keeps falling over and tumbling off. I did not anticipate that. Maybe we'd do better without the learning stretches.

Next is our Pattern of the Day, so I ask Joy to tell me what comes next, "Square, square, triangle. Square, square..."

"Triangle!" shouts Daniel.

"Hey! That was my question!" Joy yells at Daniel.

"Daniel, let Joy answer." I give her another one. "Circle, circle, star. Circle, circle…"

"Star!" yells Joy victoriously.

"That was so *easy*." Daniel rolls his eyes.

"Daniel, that is not helpful. You are not allowed to say her questions are easy. Now, say something nice to her, please."

"Like what?"

"Like, 'Good job, Joy!' or, 'You did it!'" I suggest.

"Good job, Joy," he mutters.

"Thank you. Okay, now Daniel's turn. Daniel, for this month you are going to fill out the weather chart. Go look out the window, and see what the weather looks like today."

Daniel runs to the window, "Sunny!"

"Great. Now get a sun picture out of this box, and tape it on the sun row on the chart, okay?" I give him the box and double-stick tape and point to the chart on the back of the door.

"I wanted to do the sun!" Joy bursts into tears.

"Sweetie, you get to do the weather chart next month. We are taking turns. You get to do the patterns this month!"

"I want to do the sun!" she cries.

"Joy, don't be a baby!" Daniel says.

"Daniel, stop! If you can't be kind to your sister, you'll be in the yellow chair." There is a yellow chair over by the map of the world that is our Time Out spot. I might be using it sooner than I thought.

"Okay, okay!"

"No, don't say it like that. Say, 'Yes, Mommy,' nicely, please."

"Yes, Mommy," he mumbles. He tapes the sun on the chart while Joy wipes her nose on her sleeve.

Okay, the opening routine might need a bit more work. I'm sure once they're used to this it will go much better. Let's move on to Joy's reading lesson.

I set the kitchen timer for twenty minutes. I got the idea of a timer from one of the older moms in my homeschool group. She swears by it. I've divided up our school day into twenty-minute segments; this is our first one.

"Joy, please go sit down at the desk," I instruct her. "It's time for your reading lesson."

"Daniel, you are going to play with Michael, then it will be your turn for your lesson." I point to the gated-off area in the corner with all Michael's toys. "You can play blocks or cars, read him a book, whatever. Okay?"

"Okay!" Daniel says, looking at all the toys in Michael's area. He seems to think that it looks like a lot more fun than the rest of the room.

"Great." I press the start button on the timer and sit down on the floor by Joy. She knows all her letters and short vowel sounds, so we are working on three-letter words. I have written letters on cards, and we are making different words. We make "cat" and she sounds it out: "C-A-T, cat!"

"Very good, Joy!" I give her a big hug.

"That's so easy!" Daniel says from the play area.

"Daniel!" I say sharply, giving him a look. "If you say that again you're in the yellow chair. Play with Michael!"

"Okay!"

"All right, Joy. That was very good. Here's your next word: H-A-T. What does that spell? Sound it out."

"H-A-T...hat!" Joy beams. She's so excited! And I'm so proud of her. We do a few more. Suddenly Michael realizes he can't get out of his play area because of the gate. He starts to cry.

"It's okay," I tell Joy and Daniel. "He'll be all right. He has to get used to being in there."

I go back to helping Joy make words.

"Mom," Daniel cries, "Michael needs you! He has a poopy diaper!"

Argh. Poop is totally not on my schedule. It's going to have to wait.

"I'll get it in a minute." I look at the timer. Twelve more minutes left. We can do this. I decide to ignore Michael and hope he'll go back to playing.

"Now we're going to read a book together," I tell Joy, who is looking worried about Michael. "You come sit in my lap, and we'll read it. See if you can figure out the name of the book." The book is *The Cat in the Hat*.

"I can't read, Mama," Joy says, "and Michael is crying."

"Well, you're learning to read. Michael will be okay. Just try it. Look at this word right here, can you sound it out?" I point to "cat."

Suddenly Joy realizes what book it is. "Oh, *The Cat in the Hat*!" she cries.

"Yes! That's right!" I know she didn't read the words, but she figured it out. "This word says 'the' and this word says 'in.' See, if you can sound it out: C-A-T... cat."

"Maaaa-maaaa!" Michael is wailing at the top of his lungs. I sneak a peek at him. He has his chubby arms through the bars of the baby jail, I mean gate, and is reaching out to me. His face is all red and soaked with tears. This is completely stressing me out.

It's okay. He'll be all right. He'll calm down.

Joy and I keep trying to concentrate on *The Cat in the Hat*, but it's hard to hear with all the screaming.

Finally the timer beeps and I go get Michael. That was the longest twenty minutes *ever*. Michael never calmed down. This is terrible. I pick him up and wipe off his sweet, red, crying face.

"Baby, I'm sorry." I kiss his cheeks and hug him.

"Maa-maah! Nuh?" This means, "Can I nurse?"

I decide for the next twenty minutes to keep him with me and nurse him while we do Daniel's spelling lesson. I can't put him back in that baby jail. I lay him on a blanket on the floor and start to change his diaper.

"Daniel, please get your spelling book and a pencil and go sit at the desk," I instruct him, after we have recovered a bit. I reset the timer for twenty minutes.

"What do I do?" Joy asks. The schedule says it's time for her to play with Michael, but he's not standing for any more of that.

"How about you work with the counting bears?" I suggest. I get them out of the cabinet and set them on her little table. "Just match the bear to the dot, okay?"

"Okay, Mommy!" Joy settles down happily with the colored counting bears.

I turn around to start Daniel on his spelling and see him staring out the window.

"Daniel, what are you supposed to be doing?" I ask him. I sit down on the floor by the desk and start to nurse Michael who has been pitifully saying "Nuh? Nuh, Mama?"

"Oh! I forgot! Sorry, Mom! What was I supposed to be doing again?" Daniel asks, genuinely confused.

"Get out your spelling workbook and a pencil, please." I am trying to be patient.

"Oh, yeah." Daniel goes over to the baskets with the workbooks. "Is this my spelling book, Mom?"

"Yes, that's it," I tell him. Oops, I forgot that today's the first day he's used it.

He stands looking at it. He looks at the cover. He looks at the back. He opens it and looks inside.

"Daniel. Pencil," I remind him. "They are in the desk, remember?" I had shown him this earlier.

"Oh, sorry, Mom!" Daniel sits down, gets his pencil box out of the desk and opens it. He deliberates for a while—should he choose the pencil with the fish or the sparkles? They're both good. There's a red one and a blue one. Which would be better? One has an eraser that's halfway gone. Then, there's a mechanical one to consider.

I am wondering if we will be up here when they are all teenagers, debating on college choices (Harvard? University of Oklahoma? Pepperdine?), and, also, still deciding on a pencil.

"Here." I pick up the one with the fish. "Just use this one." I look at the timer. Eleven minutes left.

I open his book for him. If I let him do it, it might take another hour.

"Okay!" I say in the most cheerful voice I can muster. "These are this week's spelling words! You are going to copy them here, see?"

"Oh, Mom! All of these?" Daniel's eyes are widening in disbelief. There are eight words on the list. We read over them together.

"Yes, honey, but just do what you can. Do your best and we'll do some more tomorrow, okay?"

The first word is "man." Daniel starts to write.

"Joy, how's it going over there?" I call to Joy, across the room.

"Good, Mommy. Can you come help me count?" Joy asks.

"I can't right now, sweetie. I am nursing Michael and have to help Daniel with his spelling. I'll try to help you count after this."

"Mom, I can't do it!" Daniel begins to panic. "The lines are too small! I can't write that small!" The lines are the same size as what he's been doing, they just look different.

"Daniel, you *can* do it. They're the same size. Just do your best. Make an 'm.'"

Daniel purposely does a terrible, extra-shaky "m." I absolutely hate it when he does this. He is acting like he can't do it, and I've seen him write an *"m"* plenty of times.

I look him in the eye. "Daniel. You know how to write an 'm.' You have to write at least four of these words before you can play this afternoon. Do your best. You are not being honest if you pretend you can't do something that you really can do."

"I can't, Mom! Why don't you trust me?" Daniel starts crying. I know he's frustrated, and I'm frustrated. But this child is going to write these four words if it takes us all day. I breathe deeply and try to calm down.

"Daniel, I want you to do your best, okay? I'm going to let you work and go sit with Joy for a bit." I decide maybe he'll do better without me next to him. I go over to see what Joy is doing and help her count some of her bears. After about one minute the timer beeps.

"Whaaaat?" Daniel is in anguish. "The timer beeped? I'm not done!"

"I know, honey. It's okay. You can finish later."

"But does that mean I can't play this afternoon? Mom, please don't make me miss play time!" He starts crying again.

Michael is now crying, too. Joy is tired of the bears. I look at Daniel's paper and he's written one word: "man." In twenty minutes. We are never going to get anything done. I feel bad that this is so hard for Daniel, but why does he have to get all panicked about it? If he would just try instead of freaking out, that would be helpful.

"We'll figure it out later," I say with a sigh. "I'll help you during Michael's nap, okay?" Which means we won't get our reading done. At this pace school is going to take twelve hours a day.

On our schedule I had Circle Time, then Math Time, but I decide to skip those. We go outside for a walk.

*****

After the walk, I put Michael down for his nap and go back upstairs with Daniel and Joy. They are supposed to be doing a journal about "What Did the Sky Look Like to You?" Instead they have brought their stuffed animals upstairs and are pretending to have school in the closet. I decide we'll skip Journal Time today and just snuggle up and read.

I gather a few books and they lean in next to me, and we read—a few pages of a book by Lynn Cheney about America, a story about Balto the dog, and "The Princess and the Pea." I let them color on clipboards on the floor as I read.

It is so nice and quiet and peaceful. This was what I imagined school would be like. I ask Daniel to work on his spelling while Joy and I clean up the counting bears. He actually finishes his three other words with minimal complaining. Then I give them stickers to put on today's square on the calendar.

As we finish up, I hear Michael crying. Seriously? How can he be awake already? I send the kids in to entertain him while I make lunch.

Now we are all sitting outside in the sunshine eating our sandwiches. The kids have juice boxes, and I have a Diet Coke.

Today was exhausting, and it's only one o'clock. But. It is only the first day. The kids need a chance to get used to the routine. I'll work with Michael to get used to his play area, maybe five minutes at a time.

Plus, I'm probably extra tired and irritable because I got up early today to exercise. Once I get used to the routine and get to bed earlier, I will have more patience with everyone.

I'm sure it will get easier.

2010/2011 School Schedule – **Revised**

| | |
|---|---|
| | Sleep until some child makes me get up |
| 8:00 | Breakfast |
| **SCHOOL (upstairs or kitchen table)** | |
| 9:00 | spelling or math lesson for Daniel, reading or math lesson for Joy |
| 10:00 | Nature walk outside & snack |
| 11:00 | Michael's nap – Reading Time |
| 1:00 | Lunch |
| 2:00 | Rest for Daniel & Joy / Julianne does housework (mostly while holding Michael) |
| 3:00 | TV time – Curious George/Sid the Science Kid |
| 4:00 | Play outside |
| 5:30 | Dinner |
| 6:30 | Daddy home & Mommy goes far, far away |
| 8:00 | Bed |

# ~ October ~

I am sitting in the church nursery room at homeschool co-op. Someone backed out of co-op at the last minute, and we got their spot. Now we look forward to seeing our friends every Friday morning. Daniel has first-grade-level classes in anatomy, geography, P.E., Spanish, and music. Joy is in the preschool class and has reading, games, music, P.E., and playtime. Michael is in the baby nursery and toddles around with his little baby friends.

I get to sit and talk to the other mommies. Priceless.

There are four moms in the nursery this hour: myself, Lisa, Sabrina, and Elizabeth. Sabrina, Elizabeth, and I are younger moms starting out on this homeschooling journey, so we feel like Lisa is our mom, too. We try to extract all the wisdom from her brain in the short hour we have together.

Lisa keeps us entertained with stories of life out in the country with her seven kids. She's only technically schooling five of them, because the baby and three-year-old aren't in school yet, but still. Five is enough.

Lisa sits in a rocking chair, trying to extricate her curly black hair from the determined fist of a six-month-old. Sabrina and I are in other rocking chairs, watching the babies play happily. Sabrina is tall and slim with long ebony hair. Today she's wearing skinny jeans, high-heeled boots, and a turquoise shirt. Sabrina was born and raised in Colombia and always looks like a Fabulously Fashionable Latin Lady. She is sipping on her

Starbucks mocha, making me wish I had money left in my weekly budget for Starbucks.

Ever since we got back from California, John's work has been a little slow, and he's worried. He would never say that, but he is. An accounting-manager friend of his was laid off and has been looking for work for *eight months*. With the economy the way it is, a few clients have put their non-essential work on hold, and John's division is way behind their numbers for this quarter. He wants us to stick to our budget and try to squirrel away any extra money, "just in case." So, no Starbucks for us for a while. We have implemented austerity measures.

The other mom in the room is Elizabeth, who is changing a baby's diaper on the other side of the nursery. She is wearing faded jeans with some cool embroidery on one leg—I bet she did that herself. Even though it's October, she's wearing beaded flip-flops, and when she leans over to pick up a diaper bag I catch a glimpse of the butterfly tattoo on her lower back. Elizabeth has fiery red hair, a raucous laugh, and enough spunk to make life interesting. She's awesome.

Elizabeth and her husband have been through the fire— they became believers in rehab in their twenties. Her husband is a teacher now, so they have three kids and virtually no money, but she has seen God work miracles in their life so often that she has no doubt He will continue to do so.

"Lay still, you little rascal!" Elizabeth is trying to wrestle the squirming baby into a diaper and then his clothes.

"Like ropin' a calf," Lisa laughs.

"Whew!" Elizabeth finishes changing the diaper, sits the baby on the ground, then plops down beside him, looking exhausted.

"How's school going for you, Jules?" Lisa asks, after everyone's settled.

"Awful," I say matter-of-factly. "Awfully, awful, awful. You?"

"What's wrong?" Lisa is so sympathetic. And focused. I guess it comes with having so many kids. She spots a toddler starting to climb the bookcase, pulls him down, and hands him a book, all while holding a baby and remaining intensely focused on what I'm saying.

"Homeschooling is crazy hard," I say. "I'm sorry, but anyone who says it's not is either lying or delusional. I know you are doing this with multiple children and a toddler and a baby, but it's killer hard for me. Maybe I'm not cut out to homeschool."

"Now that's not true," Lisa says. "Remember, I have older kids too. I mean, Sarah is twelve; she helps a lot. Jonah plays with the younger ones all the time. Plus, they can do a lot of schoolwork independently. You're still in the stage where you have to teach them everything. You have to sit beside them for every lesson."

"Yes. That's true! And they all want me at one time!" I am complaining here, but I don't care. "It's so hard, way harder than last year when Michael slept all the time. There's no break. I dream about sending my children off to a sweet, happy school and having at least the baby's naptime to sweep the floor, unload the dishwasher, or sit down and eat a meal that is still hot without two other little people asking me for things.

"The kitchen is always a mess. I'm chronically behind on laundry. During school upstairs, Michael wants my undivided attention. He's jealous if I'm even talking to Daniel or Joy. He wants to nurse about a hundred times a day, pulling at my shirt. What do I do with him?"

"Have you tried Blanket Time, where he plays on a blanket with toys?" asks Sabrina, sipping her latte. Blanket Time always sounds so good in theory. I think people whose children are older than three have forgotten what it's like to have toddlers. Sabrina's only daughter is seven.

"Sort of," I answer. "I tried putting him in this gated-off area, but he cries the whole time. Constantly. It stresses us all out. I can't do it."

"So what do you do?" Lisa asks.

"I end up nursing him, because at least it keeps him quiet so we can do school. But I'm tired of it. He's sucking the life out of me.

"And," I continue, "Michael's off the bottom of the growth chart so I do need to find a way to get him to eat more or the doctor wants to do all these tests. I know he's healthy and fine; but it's one more thing to think about—spelling, math, reading, writing, laundry, crying baby, malnourished baby, feeding the kids, feeding myself, losing weight, oh, and my husband? I forget about him all the time. He's totally ignored and mistreated. I barely remember to feed poor John."

"I alternate between peanut butter and jelly sandwiches and pasta with butter for dinner," Elizabeth pipes up from her spot on the floor. She always makes me feel better. She's a total mess. I love her. "Sometimes I throw in a pizza for a treat."

"How do all these women do it?" I ask, looking around at them all. "How can they do school and ministry and have clean houses and cook fabulous dinners and still be nice to their husbands? What is wrong with me?"

"Okay, first of all, they probably have kids older than yours," Sabrina says, in her gorgeous Colombian accent. "It's a whole different world, remember? You have a toddler right now. You can't get anything done with a toddler." Okay, fine, maybe she does remember what it's like to have a toddler.

"And," Elizabeth chimes in, "no one does *all* those things. You are lumping everyone together in your head. The moms who are doing tons of ministry aren't homeschooling; their kids are in school. The moms who have immaculate houses aren't doing art projects with their kids like I know you do."

This is true. We do a lot of art projects. Yesterday we gathered maple leaves on our walk and painted watercolor pictures of them.

Sabrina continues, "You know, if some woman *is* doing all those things maybe she shouldn't be. Maybe she's wearing herself out doing things for other people and leaving nothing for her husband and herself. Maybe it would be better to save some energy for a little hanky-panky with her husband that night." She wiggles her dark eyebrows suggestively at us.

"Sabrina!" I gasp.

"Well! Maybe it would! Maybe all these husbands would *rather* have a peanut butter and jelly sandwich for dinner and have some action that night."

"Guarantee it!" Elizabeth says, and we all crack up.

"Have you tried doing school during Michael's nap?" Elizabeth suggests, after we all calm down.

"I *am* doing it during nap time. That's when we do our Reading Time. Michael only sleeps for two hours."

"Hmm. All I know to tell you is to keep praying for wisdom, Jules. I know God will help you figure something out." Lisa says, rather unhelpfully, I think. I was hoping she would tell me what to do.

"Homeschooling is *hard*, Jules, it just is. But most things that are worth doing aren't easy." Elizabeth adds. I know she's speaking from experience. "You know one thing I've done? Sometimes, when I have to work with Chloe, we do school in the bathroom. I let the boys take a bath and color on the tile walls with sidewalk chalk, and Chloe and I sit on stools and do our lesson." Chloe is ten; the boys are four and two.

"Really?" I giggle, picturing Chloe doing math lessons in the bathroom.

"Hey, whatever works. It's not something you'd see on the cover of a homeschool magazine, but it sure helps me keep the boys out of trouble."

"That's a great idea! I'll try anything." I smile gratefully at her. "Anyway, enough about me. How's life at your house?"

"Actually," Elizabeth pauses ceremoniously, "I have some news—we're expecting!"

"Congratulations!" We all start shrieking in excitement. The babies are looking at us in alarm, so we quiet down.

"And," she adds dramatically, "it's *twins!*" No wonder she looks so exhausted.

"No way!" I gasp.

"I know!" she says. "What are the odds?"

"Oh, wow, Elizabeth, what are you going to do?" Sabrina looks worried for her. We all know money is tight at her house.

"I have no idea," Elizabeth says, honestly. "But I know God will take care of us."

"With every one of my kids I'd think, 'How can I do this with one more?'" Lisa tells her with a smile, "and now I look at them and think, 'What would I do if they weren't here?'"

"Exactly," breathes Elizabeth, with tears in her eyes. She knows exactly how precious these little lives are. She has lost several babies to miscarriages. And, during her wild years before she was married, she got pregnant with her boyfriend at the time. He offered to pay for her to end the pregnancy, but something stopped her from doing it. That baby was Chloe. She has told me that she looks at Chloe all the time and thinks how close she came.

"So," said Elizabeth, "it will be crazy for a while, but I know how fast those baby years go. We'll manage somehow."

"When are you due?" Sabrina asks.

"April," Elizabeth says, "but with my history, my doctor said she'd be thrilled if I make it to Saint Patrick's Day." Both of Elizabeth's boys were born pre-term, and they had some scary moments in the NICU. "I told her that was perfect since I have Irish in me, right? Two baby leprechauns."

Now I feel like a dork for complaining so much. At least I'm not pregnant with twins.

*****

We switch classes, and I go into the preschool class for the second hour of co-op. The class happens to be all girls. They are so cute.

Joy loves to dress herself, and she hasn't been throwing fits about her clothes lately, so I've let her have that freedom.

Today she is wearing rainbow-striped bellbottoms, a lime-green sweater with a lollipop on it, red Hello Kitty snowflake socks, a polka-dot jacket, and sunglasses. And her white patent leather Easter shoes and her white Easter hat, of course. Because Easter now comes in October.

"She is so adorable." Elizabeth is in this classroom with me again this hour.

"I know," I say, very un-humbly. "I took a picture of her this morning. She has her own definite fashion sense. Daniel, on the other hand, would wear one of his four Star Wars LEGO shirts every day if I'd let him."

Lisa told me a few years ago that she lets her kids wear whatever they want, within reason, as long as they can handle it if she says no to something. "Who cares? They'll worry about matching soon enough," she told me. I've adopted that philosophy.

Joy runs up to me when I come in her classroom. "Mommy!" she squeals delightedly.

"How's my precious girl?" I ask her, kneeling down to her level.

"I kill you!" she rasps in an evil voice and pulls a plastic dagger out from the back of her pants, then runs off to play pirates with the other girls in the class. Nice.

Elizabeth and I are going to do a collage project with the class, but we let the girls play a few more minutes.

"How's Daniel?" Elizabeth asks.

"Oh, he's good. School's a bit of a struggle, but he's a sweet little boy. Joy hits him all the time, and he never even retaliates. He is quirky though; he gets these phrases stuck in his head, so he'll say them about three hundred times a day. The other day it was 'Zickeybird.' I would ask 'Daniel, would you like more milk?' and he'd stare at me and say, 'No, I'd like some Zickeybird, please? Or, maybe a Zickeybird.'"

"Wow, that's enough to drive you crazy." Elizabeth's green eyes widen.

"Totally insane," I agree. "And he's always coming up with these complicated projects. He'll come to the kitchen and say, 'Mom, I need some boxes to build something.' I'm thinking, 'Why? And where are you going to put this creation?' His room is pretty full with Michael's crib, LEGOs everywhere, and a hideout he made from PVC pipes. So I asked him why he wanted boxes and he said, 'So I can make a refrigerator. And I'm going to cut up some more cardboard for food.' It was such a great, creative idea I couldn't say no, but it means we now have to navigate around a cardboard refrigerator when we clean his room."

"They are so weird, these little people," Elizabeth laughs. "But they keep things interesting, don't they? You're nice to let them do these things. I'm mean. I'd probably say no."

"I know you would. I want to learn to be mean too. I'm working on it." I laugh. We both know she's not mean at all, she just has a tiny house, so she has no room for superfluous refrigerators.

"Hey, want to go to the pumpkin patch with us next Tuesday?" Elizabeth always does fun things.

"We should stay home and do school." I am trying to be diligent about it.

"No, you shouldn't!" Elizabeth persuades me. "You need a break. Plus, you'll be learning about...pumpkins!"

"True! And animals!" I remember, thinking of the petting zoo.

"Yes, and…um…hay!" Elizabeth laughs.

"Okay, let's do it! Too bad we can't all go in one car."

"I know," Elizabeth says, "But my car is a pit anyway."

"Oh, I guarantee mine's worse." I am sure of it. "You know that poem about the Statue of Liberty, where it says, 'wretched refuse of our teeming shore'?"

"Yes?" she says quizzically.

"That's my car. Wretched refuse. I told John I was going to name the front seat Filth and the back seat Squalor. Then I could say accurately that we drive around in Filth and Squalor."

Elizabeth laughs. "I found a sippy cup under my seat from two weeks ago. With milk in it."

"That's nothing!" I assure her. "I've found mold, sour milk, half eaten sausages, and pancakes."

"Fruit flies," Elizabeth counters, raising an eyebrow at me.

"I have your fruit flies. And I raise you—bugs."

"I've had bugs."

"Do you know what happens when bugs get under the carpet mat on the floor in the summer?" I can't resist the challenge. "They lay eggs."

"*No!*"

"And the eggs hatch. And then you have worms. Maggots. In. Your. Car." I shudder. "I totally freaked out when I saw them. I called a babysitter to come over right then so I could go clean out the car. It was revolting. I banned eating in the car *forever.* But it only lasted two weeks."

"Wow," Elizabeth breathes in newfound respect. "That is bad. I've never had maggots."

I can't help but feel oddly triumphant. I told her my car was worse.

## JOY

### ·GROCERY STORE BINGO·

| napkins | cran-berries | milk | apples |
|---------|--------------|--------|--------|
| turkey | rolls | nutmeg | butter |

## Daniel

| milk | turkey | rolls | spinach |
|------|--------|-------|---------|
| pie crust | eggs | pumpkin | onions |

# ~ November ~

Why did I decide to do this? When John and I were trying to figure out what to do for Thanksgiving, I really didn't feel like another trip, by car or plane. Plus, a trip wasn't in our budget. We usually alternate spending holidays with my family and John's. This year was his parents' turn.

We hadn't seen John's parents since Michael's birthday party, and we hadn't seen Dave and Ginger since California. I wanted to avoid John's family coming for Christmas—I could only imagine the Gift Extravaganza of Magnificent Proportions that would have turned into. So, I invited everyone here for Thanksgiving.

Good plan, Julianne. You're overwhelmed anyway, why not plan an enormous meal and invite houseguests?

Everyone's getting in tomorrow. Which means I *have* to go to the grocery store today. I usually try to have John watch the kids if I have a huge shopping trip to do, but I want to at least get the pies made before everyone arrives. Right now the kids and I are in the car heading to Walmart.

One good thing is, since we need to go to the store and cook anyway, I decided to make our Thanksgiving preparations into "school" for the next two weeks. I've already made cute three-ring binders for Daniel and Joy. They decorated the front of them with stickers and spelled out: "My Recipe Book." They helped plan the Thanksgiving meal, made the shopping list, and read over their recipes. Tomorrow they will each help me cook one or two things. I figure they will be practicing reading comprehension, following directions, writing, spelling, math, and the practical skill of cooking. It's our own little Thanksgiving unit study!

Plus, I can't make myself go up to the schoolroom anymore.

The other day, Joy asked what we were doing, and I told her "school." She burst into tears.

"I *hate* school!" she sobbed. I felt like doing the same.

I think this will be a nice break for all of us.

Daniel is in the back of the car munching happily on his pancakes. Michael is in his car seat contentedly eating his sausage. Joy is listening to a CD on her pink headphones and singing between sips of chocolate milk. I am eating my (hot!) bacon, egg, and cheese biscuit and drinking a Diet Coke. Have I mentioned I love McDonald's? And headphones in the car. I *love* headphones in the car. The kids can listen to the same CD ten thousand times, and I can listen to Garrison Keillor read the day's poem on the radio. It's glorious.

Joy is singing along with the CD, "Sacramento, California; Sacramento, California. Phoenix, Arizoooona; Phoenix Arizoooona. Sampa Fe, New Mexico; Sampa Fe, New Mexico. Austin, Te-yak-sis; Austin, Te-yak-sis. Uh-huh."

We bought this Audio Memory CD for Daniel's co-op class, but Joy is picking up the songs without even trying. She thinks it's fun. Maybe I'll get that Classical Advantage CD after all and put it on to see how much the kids can absorb. Just when we're in the car. With no additional effort from me.

From the back I hear a sweet baby voice, "Mah! Sah-sah!"

Lovely. One of Michael's first sentences is, "More sausage." From McDonald's, no less. Fabulous.

We arrive at the store, and I get everyone situated in the shopping cart. I buckle Michael in the front. My strategy for him is to feed him the whole time to keep him occupied. Joy sits in the cart. Daniel walks beside the cart, trying to both stay close to me and not get squashed by the cart. Somehow he manages to get his toes under the cart's wheels or walk into a shelf every few minutes, so the task is trickier than one would think, apparently.

I hand Daniel and Joy their Bingo cards and crayons. When I do have to bring the kids to the store, we play Bingo to keep them occupied. I figure it counts as reading for Joy and spelling for Daniel. I'm honestly not sure if it makes the trip easier or harder, because they are always dropping their crayons or having me stop and wait while they cross out the word, but at least we get a little school in.

I have the list organized by aisle, so we start on the pharmacy side of the store. We get Pediasure for Michael; the doctor is making me feed it to him to help him gain weight. I grab a goldfish box, open it, and give Michael a few goldfish. Then we go to the back of the store.

"Milk. Who's got milk?" I ask.

"Mmmmm," Joy scans her card. "Mmm-iiii-llll-k. Milk. I do!"

"Me too! I found it too!" Daniel is scowling because Joy found it first.

"Daniel, let's be thankful you get to play Bingo, okay?" I am really about done with this attitude of his. We have got to work on this. "No complaining. It's Thanksgiving. I want you to work on being thankful this week. Every time you complain, you're going to say three things you're thankful for, okay?"

"Okay," Daniel sighs.

"All right," I continue, "Butter. Who's got butter?"

"I do!" Joy finds butter and draws an "x" over it with her crayon.

"I don't have butter! Why don't I have butter?" Daniel whines. Honestly. You'd think he was the four-year-old sometimes.

"Okay," I push the cart to the baking aisle, "that counts as complaining. Say three things you're thankful for."

"That counts as complaining?" Daniel seems shocked.

"Yes. It does. Three things." I scan the shelves for pumpkin.

"I'm thankful that...I get to play Bingo. And... I have a cutey, cutey baby brother." Daniel gives Michael's leg a squeeze. "And that...I have LEGOs." Okay, sure.

"Great. Thank you. Let's focus on saying thankful things, okay?" I put the pumpkin in the cart and say, "pumpkin."

"Oh, me! I have pumpkin!" Daniel happily crosses pumpkin off his card.

We wind around, getting all the items on the list, and I keep opening packages whenever Michael starts to get fussy. He has now had goldfish, pretzels, string cheese, and a juice box. Maybe I won't have to make lunch.

We're headed for the frozen pie crust when I realize I forgot the napkins. We start to go back when I smell something. Michael.

Well, he's just going to have to wait; I left the diapers in the car. We're almost done anyway. We go to the napkin aisle and I pass an older lady who sniffs loudly and gives us a look. Well, sorry!

Daniel is getting restless while I try to decide what napkins to get.

"Daniel, please stop smacking your brother in the face," I say, absent-mindedly.

"But he *likes* it!" Daniel argues. Michael does giggle whenever Daniel pats him, sort of hard, on his cheek.

"I don't care if he likes it," I say. "We don't want to teach him to smack people in the face! What if he does that to his little baby friends? They're not going to like it."

"I want to do it!" Joy stands up in the cart and leans around to pat Michael on the other cheek.

"NO! Joy, sit down! You are not allowed to smack your brother in the face!"

"But he *likes* it!" she argues, as Michael giggles again.

"I. Don't. Care. Stop doing it. And don't argue with me when I tell you something." I am giving her A Look. I give Daniel one for good measure. We have got to finish up.

I grab some napkins and throw them in the cart. Joy crosses out "napkins." I realize Daniel should have crossed off "spinach" back in the produce. Shoot. I usually try to have the game end in a tie, but I forgot to do that this time. Oh, well. It will be good practice for Daniel in not getting his way. Maybe they'll forget about Bingo. I gather the last few groceries and get in line at the checkout.

"Okay, let's get everything loaded on the belt!" I use my best cheery voice. The kids start tossing items up on the belt. They are actually a help at this point.

"Mommy," Joy suddenly has an urgent look on her face. "I have to go to the bathroom. Really badly!"

"Joy, please can you wait? We're almost done." I realize about half of the groceries are on the belt and half are still in the cart.

"No, Mommy! I can't!" Joy insists, "it's poo-poo!"

Oh, dear. I evaluate the situation: even though it's almost Thanksgiving, the store seems to be nearly deserted on this Tuesday morning. The bathrooms are within sight. Daniel is six. I decide to let them go.

"All right Daniel, I want you to take Joy to the family bathroom," I decide. "It's right over there. Go in with her, then come straight back. I'm on checkout number…" I glance up, "seven. Go straight there and straight back to number seven, okay?"

"By *ourselves*?" Daniel is my timid one. He gets nervous about doing things by himself.

"O-kay!" Joy says without hesitation. "Let's go, Daniel!" She climbs out of the cart with my help and starts running to the bathroom. Daniel decides to follow.

"Hold hands!" I call after them. "And walk, please! Walk!" They do.

I finish unloading the groceries onto the cart while silently praying: *Please let them not get kidnapped. No one would kidnap two kids from Walmart, would they? Maybe they would. And please let this checker not turn me in for negligence. She probably already thinks I'm an unfit mother because my baby is sitting here in a stinky diaper.*

A mom walks by with a toddler in her shopping cart. "Phew!" She wrinkles her nose. "Is that you, Rosie?"

"No, that would be us." I give the lady an embarrassed smile. "Sorry."

Finally all the items are rung up, and the checker is loading up the cart. I keep my eyes on the restroom the whole time and exhale when I see the kids emerge. They skip back to me, holding hands, smiling broadly.

"Hi, Mommy!" Joy sings out. "We did it! And we remembered, checkout number seven!"

"I'm so proud of you!" I say, giving them each a hug. "I knew you could do it! You are so responsible!" *Thank you, Lord, that they weren't abducted. That would be hard to explain to John.*

"You know what?" I say to the checker. "Let me just add one more thing." I throw a pack of M&M's on the belt.

I think we all deserve some M&M's.

*****

John's family arrived a few hours ago, and everyone is hanging out in the living room nibbling on cheese and crackers. What a happy place! I love Thanksgiving. Well, technically, it's not Thanksgiving until tomorrow, but close enough.

John has to work until two today, but he will be home soon. The kids and I made a pumpkin pie and a blackberry pie yesterday, and the turkey is thawing in the refrigerator. Michael is down for his nap. Daniel and Drew are in the backyard, and Maddie is painting Joy's toenails in the bathroom. Finally, the girls found something in common—nail polish.

"Julianne, I can't believe you didn't tell us you don't have a TV!" Frank says gruffly.

"We do have a TV," I say sheepishly. "It just doesn't work. I forgot. I'm sorry!"

"How can you forget that your TV doesn't work?" Dave asks. Apparently the men were planning to watch football. Oops.

"Well, the VCR/DVD player works. It's just the TV part doesn't. You could watch Dora!" I joke.

Dave does not look amused.

"We can buy you a new TV, sweetie." Vicky says, looking concerned.

"No, Vicky, it's fine! Really! I actually have been wanting to try life without TV so it's a good experiment. It's kind of nice. John is going to get an HD one soon. We're just holding off for a while." Until John is sure he is going to keep his job, I want to add, but decide against it.

"Oh, thank goodness." Frank seems relieved that someone in the family has some sense.

"And remember, that little one works." I point to the ten-inch TV in the corner, hooked up to the antenna and channel box. "That's where the kids watch PBS KIDS. So, you can watch football on that tomorrow if you want."

"I didn't bring my magnifying glass," Dave says wryly. "How do they see on that thing?"

"I don't know; they just sit really close?" I offer.

"And, what do *you* watch?" Ginger's brow is furrowed. "I can't believe you don't have cable, even."

"What do I watch?" I think for a minute. I assume she means other than kids' shows.

"Oh, I know! I have these 19 Kids and Counting DVDs that I watch sometimes." Not very often, though. Who has time to watch television?

"Those people? You're not going to have nineteen kids are you?" Vicky looks like she's only half-joking.

"I don't know. Maybe just ten." I like to scare her.

"She's kidding, Vicky," Frank says, and this time Vicky is the one that looks relieved.

"Hey, speaking of you guys being freaks, how's homeschooling going?" Dave asks with a smile.

"Oh, all right." I don't really want to get into the true awfulness of it.

"Isn't it amazing what they learn?" Ginger asks. "Last week Drew came home telling me all about the gods and goddesses of ancient Greece. And Maddie's science class is building catapults and levers. I love Dalton Prep."

Catapults and levers? Daniel would love that. I've never built a catapult or lever with him.

"And they have been studying Monet in art," Dave reaches for another cracker. "They did reproductions of one of the *Water Lilies* paintings. They turned out amazing."

"I'm getting them framed," Ginger agrees.

We've never done reproductions of Monet paintings. Joy would love *that*. I think I'm selling my kids short. All we do is go to Walmart.

"How much is the tuition?" I would normally not ask such a personal question, but Ginger never minds discussing amounts.

"It's about twenty a year." Ginger tells me. Blink, blink. Try not to hyperventilate.

"Twenty for both of them?" I ask, trying to appear calm. She means twenty thousand.

"Each. But we get a 10 percent discount since they are both enrolled."

"Wow," I say, stunned. So, *forty* thousand dollars per year. Somehow a 10 percent discount doesn't seem like a huge help.

"That's in Dallas, though. It's probably half of that in Tulsa, depending on the school," Ginger tries to reassure me. "It's totally worth it." Okay, I have to sit here and focus on breathing for a minute.

"Completely," Dave agrees. "It's just as much of an investment in their education as college."

"You know, sweetie, you can stop homeschooling any time," Vicky tells me with a concerned look on her face.

"I know," I say through clenched teeth. Remember Jules, Vicky loves you. She loves the kids. She wants the best for them. We are all on the same team.

"Are they reading this?" Frank is holding a thick book that he picked up from the library basket by the fireplace. I'm happy he's changed the subject.

"No," I laugh. "That one's mine. It's *Little Women*. It's really good, actually. I don't think I've ever read the unabridged version of it."

"I remember *Little Women*!" Ginger's eyes light up. "I remember wanting to be just like Jo—a writer. And independent." Really? She did?

"You don't write, honey," Dave reminds her.

"No, but I *could*. If I *wanted* to. *I* want to read *Little Women*," Ginger sighs wistfully.

"Um, you don't *read*," Dave adds gently.

"I do *too*!" Ginger protests.

"I mean books."

"Yes, I *do*!"

"Like what? What was the last book you read?" Dave asks, with an amused but loving look on his face.

"Umm…well…okay, other than reading to the kids, I guess I haven't read *that* many books lately. But I *should*. I *am* going to read Little Women! Along with Julianne. Then when we get together, we can discuss it. Like our own book club! Like on Oprah. Maybe Oprah will pick *Little Women,* and we can go on the show and tell what we learned!"

"Oprah's going off the air," I remind her. See, I know about current events. "But I think we should do our book club anyway! Let's do it. You read it and underline and write your thoughts in yours, and I'll do the same—I guess I'll have to get my own copy instead of the library's but that's okay—and we'll discuss it!"

"Great!" Ginger says smugly. "See, Dave, I'm in a book club! I'm very literary."

"Hey, Grandpa and Grandma, come out to the backyard! We have to show you something!" Daniel and Drew burst into the living room with red cheeks and sparkling eyes.

"Daniel, ask nicely, please; don't just order people around," I remind him.

"Oh, sorry. Grandpa and Grandma, can you please come to the backyard? You have to see what we made!" Daniel tries again. That's a little better.

"Sure, sweetie. Let me just grab my coat," Vicky says. Frank and Vicky both get their coats and follow the boys outside.

I hear the garage door go up—John must be home from work. He comes into the living room.

"Hi!" I give him a kiss. "There's something very important going on in the backyard, but come sit with us a minute first."

John gives hugs to Dave and Ginger, and then sits down on the couch.

"How's work?" Dave asks his little brother.

"Oh, okay," John says, in a voice that tells me it wasn't okay.

"What happened?" I ask, bracing myself.

"Well," John sighs, "we lost another client today."

"Seriously?" I ask. "Another one? Who?"

"Oh, a small one—Tenley Oil and Gas. It was a merger. They were bought by a Canadian company that has their own auditors; they don't need us anymore."

"Oh, man, I'm sorry," Dave says. "That's rough."

"Yeah. If it keeps up I won't have any clients left," John laughs, trying to play it off, but I know he's halfway serious. He's having to consider laying off two people as it is, people with families to support. I know this is incredibly stressful for him.

"You *will* have clients left," I tell John, "because you're brilliant and honest and work like crazy. And, whatever happens, we'll be okay. If we truly need it, God will provide it, whether it's work or clients or whatever."

"Thanks, Jules." John smiles at me. I know he appreciates me trying to reassure him, but I don't know that he's buying it. Since it's John's department having trouble, he is worried that he'll be held responsible. Or fired. He's thinking that it doesn't matter how smart or hard-working he is; he needs results.

"I'm sorry guys," Ginger says sympathetically, though I know money worries are a bit foreign to her.

"You know, I have something that might cheer you up," Ginger says, smiling. "We're planning a surprise party for Frank and Vicky's 40th Anniversary. It will be in May at our house.

We're going to invite all of their best friends and the whole family, kids included. Can you guys come?"

"Wow, I forgot this was forty years!" John says. "Of course we'll come. That's a great idea to have a surprise party."

"It was Ginger's idea," Dave says admiringly. "She throws a great party."

"I do throw a great party," Ginger concedes. "It will be in our backyard. We'll have tables and chairs set up and have a nice, fancy dinner."

"So, what can we do?" I ask. "I'm all the way in Tulsa. I don't know what I can do for a party in Dallas."

"Oh, don't worry about that!" Ginger waves her hand. "You've got plenty to do. I love planning parties. I'll take care of everything. You guys just show up."

"Great!" John says, and right in time because the back door opens and Frank pops his head in.

"John, you have to see this. Actually all of you, get your coats and come out here! You won't believe what the boys made."

Oh, dear. This could be anything. We all get our coats.

"What is it?" Joy hears something exciting going on and runs out to the living room.

"Are your toenails dry?" I stop her. I really don't want purple nail polish all over the carpet.

"Yes, Aunt Julianne, they're dry," Maddie assures me.

"Okay you guys, put on your shoes and coats—the boys have something to show us." I help Joy with her boots and coat, and we all go outside.

"We made a zip line!" Daniel announces. The boys have tied some string from the top of the fort to the lowest branches of the pear tree. Drew is up on the fort.

"Ready?" Drew yells.

"Ready!" Daniel calls back.

Drew lets go of one of Daniel's stuffed animals—a raccoon. The raccoon is duct-taped to the bottom of a wire hanger, and the hook of the hanger is looped over the string. The weight of the raccoon pulls the contraption down the string. The raccoon hurtles along the string and smacks into the pear tree. "Boom!" The boys laugh uproariously at the collision.

"Cool!" Maddie says. "I want to try!"

"Okay, go get some more stuffed animals!" Drew tells the girls. "And hangers! We can make more!"

The girls run back inside and are soon back with armfuls of stuffed rabbits, bears, and dogs. Joy has about ten wire hangers. I am wondering if duct tape comes off stuffed animals without ripping out the fur, but I decide not to spoil the fun. We'll find out.

"And, Daddy, look over here!" Daniel shouts. "We made a row of catapults with plastic spoons, and we're attacking the guys down on the bottom fort with acorns!" The boys line up a row of acorns.

"Ready, aim, fire!" Drew calls.

They fire the catapults and laugh when the acorns go flying.

"You built catapults?" Maddie says, with respect in her voice. "That's awesome! I want to see!"

"Well, we didn't really build it," Daniel explains. "The spoons are just levers."

"How does he *know* that?" Ginger asks me, impressed.

"I have no idea!" I say. "Maybe it was on Sid the Science Kid? They watch that sometimes in the afternoons. Or Curious George?" I am honestly not sure. But I'm glad John's family is impressed. Maybe they won't think I'm going to totally mess the kids up. This year, anyway.

"I think we have a book about levers, too," John adds. "And Julianne thinks things like duct tape and balls of string make good birthday presents."

"Well?" I gesture to the kids, excitedly duct taping a stuffed poodle to a hanger. "Apparently, so do they!"

"It's freezing out here! Let's go in for hot chocolate!" Vicky proposes.

"Yeah! Hot chocolate!" The kids all clamber down and run inside too, the engineering projects put on hold for a while.

We go in, and John makes cocoa with whipped cream for all of us. We hear Michael crying from the bedroom, waking up from his nap. Vicky and Ginger go get him up and play with him; they enjoy having a baby to fuss over. Vicky really is a sweet grandmother; she loves doting on the kids whenever she comes to town.

Daniel and Drew talk their dads into playing a simplified game of Risk on the dining room table. Joy picks out *Cranberry Thanksgiving* from the library basket for Grandpa to read to her on the couch in front of the fire. I didn't know Frank could look so...gentle.

It seems like everyone forgot about watching football. I think I'll break the TV at Thanksgiving every year. Or at least unplug it.

I go to the kitchen to start peeling apples for the cranberry sauce (I like to add apples to make it sweet). I am thinking about Frank and Vicky's anniversary party. I'm sure it will be amazing. When Ginger says a "fancy dinner," I know she means it. Their backyard is huge, and I'm sure it will be all decked out with flowers and lights. Frank's friends are doctors like he is or lawyers or wealthy businessmen. It will probably be a black tie event. Jeans and tennis shoes are perhaps not appropriate.

I do have to hand it to Ginger—she is really quite unselfish. Sure, she likes nice things and going to the spa, but she is incredibly generous, too. I had completely forgotten about Frank and Vicky's anniversary, and here she is planning a huge surprise party for them. I've been so consumed with my own problems, I haven't even had time to think about anything else.

That is one other benefit of having the kids in school, I realize. I'd have more time to reach out to others. Hmm. That's something to think about.

Ooh, and another thing to think about: What are John and I going to do for Frank and Vicky's gift? We have to get them *something*, even if we don't help with the party. But they already have everything. What could we possibly get them that they don't already have, something that comes even close to what all their rich friends will get them?

As I start to stir the cranberries on the stove, I overhear bits of conversation and laughter floating into the kitchen. Daniel and Drew are playing Risk with their dads: discussing war strategy, counting by fives and tens, and learning the location of Madagascar. Joy is captivated by her book: learning language and vocabulary, cadence and rhythm, wrapped up in the love of her grandfather. Michael is laughing with his aunt and grandmother as they play "This Little Piggie": strengthening those neural networks, as well as those connections of the heart.

The only one not engaged is Maddie. She sits alone on the couch texting friends on her iPhone. I love Maddie, that sweet little lady, but I'm a bit worried for her, and for my own kids. Where is all this technology taking us? Is this the world we're giving our teens? The connection of face-to-screen? No wonder they are anxious and depressed; no wonder they have deficits of attention and delight.

In Tulsa lately the schools have been trying to raise money for more technology. Like our children need *more* technology. They need less technology and more of us. They need us—to read to them, play with them, see them, hear them. I admit, TV does help me sometimes, when I absolutely have to get things done, if I'm out of energy or tired. But every time we have a TV-free week I'm grateful. Life is a bit messier, a little louder, but a lot better. I am the one who has to get out of the habit of turning on a kids' show, not the kids. They don't really care all that much. They find other things to do. Our home is more connected, more peaceful.

I look at Maddie, perfectly isolated and perfectly content, and strengthen my resolve. This is why we are going to try to limit video games and other technology even if people think we're weird, I remind myself. For one thing, plenty of studies have shown that all this animation rots children's brains, conditioning them for ever-increasing stimulation and decreased attention spans. How can a plain old book, even a good one like *Treasure Island*, ever compete with the Wii?

For another thing, I keep seeing children (and parents) so addicted to their false reality that they have become numb to the glory of the world around them: the beauty of leaves on fire with autumn color, the chill of the air on their faces, the voices of their families. Children and parents bob happily along, carried away by electronic rivers, while their lives float by them, unnoticed.

We have lots of friends whose kids play video games; we love the parents and we love the kids. We are certainly not better or worse parents because of the choices we make about texting or iPhones or TV. This is just something that's been on my heart lately.

I want to raise children who know how to be still, how to sit, how to think. I want my children to have hearts for people, not things, and to live to serve, not to be entertained. And, ultimately, I want them to learn to listen: to family and friends, to their own hearts, and to that Voice that doesn't beep and flash, that doesn't always thunder in a whirlwind or burn with fire, but that comes in a gentle whisper.

Weekly Lesson Plan

| | School Plan | School Actual |
|---|---|---|
| Weekend/Other | | |
| Copywork/Journal | M<br>T<br>W<br>R (Journal) — Go Tell It On the Mountain | none |
| D's Lessons | M (Spelling)<br>T (Spelling/Grammar)<br>W (Spelling) — Lesson #14 / Grammar #12 | ✓<br>✓ |
| | M (Math)<br>T (Math)<br>W (Math) — December worksheets | ✓ (only 2 pages front/back) |
| J's Lessons | M (Phonics)<br>T (Phonics/Grammar) — ĕ<br>W (Phonics) — Book: Ten Men | ✓<br>✓ (plus helped read 12 Days of Xmas) |
| | M (Math)<br>T (Math)<br>W (Math) — Math workbook | ✓ |
| D & J Books – Mom reads (3/day) | M<br>T<br>W — Christmas Books<br>R • Farmer Boy<br>Chapter Book: • Hudson Taylor | • Gingerbread Doll<br>• 12 Days of Xmas<br>• Xmas Miracle of Jonathan Toome<br>• Joy to the World<br>• Born on Xmas Morning<br>• Nutcracker<br>• Sleigh Bells + Snowflakes<br>• Hudson Taylor (4 chapters) |
| D's Reading Aloud (10 min/day) | M<br>T<br>W<br>R — Greg's Microscope | ✓ |
| Art/Craft | R<br>other — none | • bread dough ornaments<br>• gingerbread house |
| Other Learning (Playtime, field trips, etc.) | M<br>T<br>W<br>R — ? | • Nutcracker Ballet<br>• Nutcracker Music<br>• stringing cranberries |

Fridays – co-op/park

# ~ December ~

I am a terrible mother.

Today might possibly be the worst day of homeschooling yet.

We had to go get a few last-minute Christmas presents. I hate Christmas. Wait, I shouldn't say that. I like celebrating the birth of Jesus, but the rest of it stresses me out. Why can we not just make a birthday cake for Jesus and sing Happy Birthday and some Christmas carols? I hate having to buy presents for everyone; I hate having to get presents from everyone; I hate parties; I hate special events. Next year I want to stay home all December. Just call me Mrs. Grinch.

Today, we had to go to Target. It was freezing outside so everyone needed their socks and shoes on. You would not think this would be hard. Socks. Shoes. Daniel and Joy are six and four years old, not two.

"Guys, please get your socks and shoes on," I instructed them, making sure they heard me. I went to get Michael changed and dressed and came back. Daniel and Joy were pretending to be horses in the living room.

"Guys! *Why* do you not have your socks and shoes on?" I was so irritated at them.

"Oh, sorry Mom, I forgot!" said Daniel.

"I didn't hear you!" said Joy.

Neither of these were good answers. This happens *all the time*. I should have sent them to Time Out, or had them practice obeying my voice, or made them copy a verse on listening to your parents. But I didn't have time for that. We needed to go. I had a lot of stuff to do.

"Put. Your. Shoes. On." I said, not at all nicely. in a very mean Mommy voice. "What did I say?" I demanded.

"Put on our shoes?" They looked scared of me. Good.

"Yes. Do it. Now."

They scampered off and got their shoes on. I got everyone buckled in the car and gave them a juice box and a cheese stick to eat while we drove. I really wanted McDonald's, but I've been trying to cut back.

In the car Daniel was asking, "Mom, please can you get me the big Pharoah's Quest LEGO set for Christmas? Pleeeeze?"

"No, Daniel. I've already gotten your present. Nana and Poppy have already gotten your present. Everyone's already gotten their presents for you. We'll just have to see what they got you."

"But Mom, it's so cool! It has another flying mummy!" Daniel pleaded.

"Daniel, you have, like, fifteen LEGO sets. Can you just be content with what you have?" I swear, as soon as he gets one LEGO set he starts begging for the next one. It's exhausting.

"Actually, I only have fourteen sets. And this one is the Scorpion Pyramid! It comes with another flying mummy and the sixth and final Golden Treasure, the Golden Nemes!" Daniel was as earnest as if his very life depended on this. My brain can only listen to one sentence about LEGOs before it shuts off. I had no idea what he was talking about. He was still going, "... and two wolf guardians, Mom! And Jake and Helena! And sliding trap doors..."

"Daniel," I cut him off, "if you don't stop begging, you're losing all your LEGOs. I'm putting them in the attic. Be thankful for what you have or you're *losing them all*. For one week. I'm not kidding."

"Fine!" Daniel said, in a rude voice. I was seething. He can be so disrespectful. But I was too mad to even talk to him about it right then.

When we got to Target, Daniel and Joy had to get out of their seats, and I had to twist around and get Michael out of his seat, and get everyone's coat on in the car, including mine. Usually I end up standing outside in the frigid wind gritting my teeth while Daniel and Joy struggle to get their coats on and Michael cries. When it's freezing cold I think they actually move half as fast. So, we now have a rule: everyone must have their coats on before exiting the car.

Joy said, "I can't put my coat on, Mommy, there's not enough room in here! I can't!"

"Yes, you can, Joy. You have to."

I ended up helping her, not very nicely, into her coat. I looked at her leg. It was wet.

"Joy, why is your leg wet?" I demanded angrily.

"I don't know." She stared at me with big, frightened brown eyes.

"She spilled her juice box on it. By holding it upside down." Daniel told on her from the back seat.

"Joy? Did you hold your juice box upside down?" I knew the answer, so I don't know why I asked the question.

"Satan did it."

"Satan did not spill your juice box."

"Yes, he did!" Joy insisted.

"No. He. Didn't. You lied to Mommy so you're in Time Out when we get home." You would think I had told her she'd have her head cut off.

"No! Mommy! Noooooooooo! I'm sorry! I'm sorry! I didn't mean to!" Joy was screaming and crying.

"I'm sorry. You will be in Time Out when we get home. And we are going to Target. You'll have to have a wet leg."

"Noooo, Mommy! It's too cold! I'll freeze!"

"You won't freeze in one minute. You'll be fine."

"Mom, it's so cold. You can't let her be wet." Daniel was genuinely concerned.

"Daniel, stay out of it. This is between Joy and me." I appreciated his caring for his sister and all, but this was none of his business.

"We're going in to the store and you'll be fine," I told her. "You need to calm down, *now*. We are going in."

Miraculously, nothing disastrous happened at Target—just lots of me being mean and making them cry. Then we came home and more me being mean and making them cry. Because, as I've already mentioned, I'm a terrible mother.

I tried to make Daniel and Joy do math at the kitchen table, but they kept distracting each other, and I kept sending them to Time Out.

This is where I should have given up, but I didn't. I kept heedlessly plowing full-steam ahead, ignoring any warnings of impending doom, like a smaller and crankier version of the Titanic.

I had planned to make a triple batch of a few recipes to go in the freezer so that when my family comes for Christmas we'd have food ready. I don't like when family is in town, and I have to spend my time going grocery shopping and cooking. So, I planned to make triple batches of meatloaf, chili, and chicken curry, which sounded easy enough. It wasn't.

I kept having to stop chopping vegetables to get Michael out of trouble. He got into the craft cabinet in the laundry room and spilled beads all over the floor. He climbed up the stepstool into the sink and turned the water on. (He was trying to brush his teeth.) He pried the lid off his sippy cup and spilled milk all over his chair and the table, getting it on Joy's math book and making her cry.

Somehow, despite all this, by two o'clock I had the meatloaves made and in the freezer. I had the soups on the stove simmering. I gave the kids bananas for lunch. I was getting ready to put Michael down for his nap.

I went out of the kitchen to get Joy out of Time Out for the four hundredth time that day. I came back in and found that Michael had learned to pull a chair across the room, reach up to the island, get the spices, and unscrew the lids. *Thank goodness he didn't go the stove*—the thought momentarily swept over me. It was soon replaced by dismay as I looked down. Michael had opened and dumped out three entire containers—cumin, garlic powder, and red curry—and was now sitting on the floor sweeping his arm from side to side making patterns in it and spreading it. All. Over. The floor.

Daniel started laughing. I lost it.

"This is *not* funny!" I told him angrily. "You think it's funny? You come clean it up."

"What? What did I do?" Daniel yelled back at me. "Why am I in trouble again?"

"Because you don't listen to me!" I snapped. "You and Joy ignore me and fight and don't do what I ask you to do! It's not funny when I have more work to do."

"I said I'm sorry!" Daniel said with wide eyes, filling with tears. "Why do you always yell at me?"

He looked so small and defeated suddenly that my heart melted. He didn't mean it. He's only six. They are only children.

I sank down on the floor, out of the way of most of the spice mess, and whispered, "Come here, buddy."

He came over, and we hugged and cried. "I'm so sorry," I told him, looking into his dear face. He still looks like a baby sometimes, with that little nose sprinkled with freckles and his big blue eyes. "I shouldn't have yelled at you."

I held Daniel while he sobbed and sobbed. Joy came in from the other room and sat with us, crying too. She's only a little baby herself. Why am I so mean to her?

"Mommy, you break my heart into pieces," Daniel said through tears. Oh, that's awful. That's almost worse than if I was hitting them. They are scared of me and feel like I am beating up their hearts. I cried with them.

"It's not your fault, you guys." I tried to explain to them, gesturing to the spices and beads all over the floor, the spilled milk on the table. "It's just—all of this. Michael has been making such big messes all day. I shouldn't yell, though. That's not an excuse."

"We have too many kids," Daniel said softly. How can he think that? That is horrible. I am an awful mother if he thinks that I wish I didn't have them all. But I probably have been acting like that.

"Oh, no, honey! No, no, no! You are all so precious to me." Tears were pouring down my face. "Michael is so precious to me. I can't imagine what we'd do without him." We looked over where Michael was sitting in only a diaper with his chubby baby legs out in front of him and spices all over his round tummy. He banged himself in the head with an empty plastic spice bottle to get us all to laugh. We did.

"Oh, no, this is not because we have too many kids." I tried to reassure them enough that they would really believe it.

"I love each of you so dearly. Mommy is just a sinner, like all of us, and I messed up. I really, really messed up. When I get angry like that it's not your fault; it's my fault. I was wrong. Will you forgive me?"

They both said yes and we prayed for forgiveness. I kissed them and held them tight.

"You know what?" I said, after we had all our sniffles and tears out. "Let's go to the YMCA."

"Yay!" they cried. We never do that anymore, and I'm not sure why. They get to color and play basketball, and I get to go for a run and have a break.

I turned off the burners on the stove and let the soup cool down while we were gone. I could bag it up when we got back. I got Michael washed up and dressed, though he still smelled like an Indian restaurant. The kids put on shoes and we left.

I am on the treadmill now, thinking over the whole day.

What am I doing? What is the point of homeschooling my children if they don't know they are loved? Better to have them in school and know that their Mom loves them than think I can do it all when I obviously can't.

I am thinking and praying as I jog. I read over the words on my memory verse pack, "Unless the Lord builds the house, they labor in vain who build it." Psalm 127:1.

I don't want to build my house. I am doing a crummy job. I want the Lord to build it.

*I don't have to homeschool.* I pray. *I want to do what you want, Lord. Make me a good Mommy to my children, and I pray you would build this house.*

I flip the index card over and read the next verse: "Behold, children are a gift of the Lord, the fruit of the womb is a reward." Psalm 127:3, NASB.

*Lord, help me treat my children like the gift they are. Please show us what to do for their school. Help me see them as you see them—precious in your sight, always. Amen.*

\*\*\*\*\*

I tell John the whole story that night in bed.

"I don't know if I should be doing this," I cry to him, honestly. "Maybe your mother is right; maybe Joy and Daniel would be better off in school. Daniel would have a real teacher." I imagine his teacher standing at the school door in the morning welcoming him with a smile. She'd be wearing a sweater with apples knitted on it; she would smell like lilacs and have a voice like Bambi's mother. "I just yell at them all the time."

"You don't yell at them *all* the time. I think today was particularly stressful," John reasons with me. He is such a good husband. He was even sneaking up to the schoolroom each evening to straighten it up and get it ready for the next day. You know, back when we used to go up to the schoolroom.

"But, John, *every* day is stressful. I may not yell, but they know when I am angry and irritated at them."

"Well, I think you are doing a great job, honey." John hugs me while I cry. "They are learning. They are growing in their character; I can see it. They aren't perfect, but they are growing. You aren't perfect either, though. We all mess up. You are forgiven. God's mercies are new every morning."

"I know," I sniffle, "but I'll mess up again tomorrow, you know? Maybe this is not what I should be doing."

"Well, we can find ways to get you more breaks or help," John says. "If you're overwhelmed, we can make some changes. Maybe you could go to the YMCA more often. You could get a babysitter once a week. And, if you want, we can look into putting Daniel at Redbud this spring. They might let him start after the break." What? We've talked about Redbud Academy, but John has been so worried about his job that I didn't think that was even an option.

"Really? Can we afford it?" I ask.

"We could afford it this spring—we could take the tuition money out of savings. I'm not sure what we'd do next year, but we can see what happens. Public school is always an option, too."

John and I have talked before about public school. We don't like the agenda in public schools, but there are other issues. The schools in our district are way behind academically, plus the schools have been reorganized so our kids would have to ride a bus thirty minutes each way to get to and from school. Or I'd have to drive them, which means Michael would spend two hours in his car seat every day, minimum. We'd have to supplement academically and have much less time with our children. Or, we'd have to move so we'd be in a better school district. Neither one of us is crazy about those options.

"I want you to be happy." John strokes my hair. "So if homeschooling is making you miserable, we don't have to do it. Why don't we both think and pray about it over Christmas. I don't know that we've ever really asked God what He wants as far as schooling; we just sort of decided to do it."

"That's true," I sniffle. "Okay. Let's think and pray about it and we can call the school when they start back if we want to do it."

"Perfect." John kisses me on the top of my head. "You're doing a good job, Julianne."

"I'm doing a terrible job," I sniffle back. "But, thanks."

"No school until after the new year," John decides.

I love that man.

\*\*\*\*\*

My family came in this week. My parents are staying at a hotel. Holly, her husband, Jay, and Emma are staying in our guest bedroom upstairs. We have had wonderful days of reading Christmas books by the fire, singing carols, and hanging ornaments. I only got out for one event: I took Joy to a children's ballet performance of *The Nutcracker* on Sunday evening. The tickets were only twelve dollars each, and the cast is almost entirely children.

Joy looked like a baby angel: her round cheeks were flushed with excitement, and her brown eyes sparkled with happiness at going on a special Mommy date. I had brushed her blonde hair back from her soft face, braided it into two "loopidies," and tied them each with white satin bows. She looked a lot like Gretel, the five-year-old on *The Sound of Music*, with those cute buns on either side of her head.

She wore her fanciest dress, a white tulle and satin flower-girl dress, white tights, and white patent leather shoes. (I'm not sure what the rule is on white patent leather shoes in winter, but whatever.) She looked like she could be in the show as one of the snowflake ballerinas.

The Nutcracker performance was wonderful. Joy sat on my lap the whole time, still and quiet. She loved getting to see all the dancers, though she was a bit confused about the dream-inside-a-play-on-a-stage aspect. Probably twenty people stopped her to ask her if she was one of the ballerinas and tell her how beautiful she looked; she just glowed. I tell her what I always tell her, "You know what's even prettier than the way you look?" She rolls her eyes but smiles when I tell her: "Your heart." It's true; she's a precious little darling of a girl.

Now we're home and I've tucked a sleeping Joy into bed, tulle dress and all. Daniel and Michael are already asleep.

Holly comes downstairs from putting Emma to bed in the Pack-N-Play; she joins me in the kitchen. Everyone else is in the living room watching *White Christmas*. I make some hot tea and microwave popcorn and get out a bar of Christmas chocolate (I bought it for myself so I decided I could open it early).

"So, the Nutcracker was good?" Holly starts to work on something over by the blender.

"It was great. Joy loved it. She told me that she wants to be in it next year. I should do things alone with her more often." I notice what my sister is doing and pause. "What are you *making*?"

So far on the counter Holly has: orange juice, frozen bananas and blueberries, and a bunch of kale. She is washing off the green kale leaves and putting them in the blender.

"Green smoothie. It's my new thing." She adds some frozen bananas to the blender. "You should try it!"

"Uh, no thanks. I don't like kale." I'll stick to my bar of dark chocolate with almonds.

"I don't either!" Holly says, "but you can't even taste the kale! It tastes like a Jamba Juice smoothie. And you're getting those dark green veggies in. This month on my blog, I'm doing a Cruciferous Veggie Challenge. They are proven cancer-fighters, you know. Whoever thinks of the most ways to use cruciferous veggies in kid-friendly ways wins."

"Wow, you really are a *Superfood Mommy*!" This is the name of Holly's blog.

"I know, it's so weird, but I love it. I love learning all about nutrition and how to feed my family." Holly does seem to have a healthy glow about her.

"Maybe you could have a McDonald's Challenge," I suggest. "I'd totally win that one."

"Hands down." John comes into the kitchen and takes a bite of my chocolate bar. Apparently the movie is over. "I balance the checking account online. Jules uses the debit card everywhere, so I can see each transaction. Guess what the record was for trips to McDonald's in one month?"

Here we go again.

"I don't know, eight?" Holly guesses. Amateur.

"Twenty-seven," John says, waiting for the gasp. Holly gasps.

"Okay, but that was months ago!" I protest. "I've cut way back! And, in all fairness—a lot of times we go through the drive-thru for drinks or snacks. We'll go through for chocolate milk and iced tea and apples or something. "

"Or Diet Coke," John points out.

"Or Diet Coke," I concede. "Hey, this mothering thing is hard. So I'm an addict. It's just pop. At least it's not crack, right?"

"True. It is better than crack." Holly blends up her concoction. It turns a weird purply-green color. She pours it into a glass.

Mom comes into the room to sit around the table with me and John. Dad and Jay are still talking in the living room.

"They started discussing rig counts so I thought I'd come in here with you girls." Mom notices what Holly is doing. "What is *that*?"

"Green smoothie. It's so good. Here, you have to taste it." Holly gets her a straw. Mom sips.

"Ooh, that is really good! Julianne, you have to try this!" Mom hands me the glass. Fine—I'll try it.

Okay, that's not bad. Sort of good, in fact. You can't even taste the kale.

"You like it!" Holly crows. "I can tell! Great, I'll put that on the blog. You're a tougher critic than most kids, and if you like it..."

"I could do that." I am surprised to admit it. "And, it would be easier than a salad." Who has time to eat a salad? It takes forever. I could drink my smoothie, get some healthy greens in, and still have an extra hand to correct a math worksheet. Plus, I still have about eight pounds to lose, so this might be a good lunch for me.

"See, sometimes your little sister is right!" Holly smiles at me. "Next month's challenge is making kefir. After that I'm deciding between sprouted lentils and fermented foods. Or possibly, bone broth."

John snorts. "I think you're on your own with those, Holly."

"How's Michael doing with his eating?" Holly sits down with us at the table. "Is he gaining weight?"

"Yes, finally." I help myself to a few more sips of her smoothie. "I cut down to nursing him just first thing in the morning and last thing at night, and he's eating much better. At his eighteen-month checkup he was almost back on the growth chart! The doctor didn't even threaten any tests."

"What did you do when he pulled at your shirt to nurse?" Holly asks. "Emma has started to do that, and it drives me nuts." Emma is fifteen months old.

"I started saying no." I tell Holly. "A friend told me that: to say 'no nurse,' give him a sippy cup of milk instead, and not give in whenever he pulls at my shirt. It took about a week of tears, and me telling him "no nurse" about eight hundred times, but it worked. He stopped asking. Thank goodness."

"But La Leche League people always say, "Don't offer; don't refuse.'"

"Yes, well," I say, taking a sip of my tea, "they weren't nursing my kid. I was. And I was tired."

"Yes, and at least you're still nursing him, honey," my mom encourages me. "He's still getting all those immune-boosting nutrients. You're a good mom."

"Thanks, but I sure don't feel like that sometimes." I tell her about my recent breakdown. "I don't know why I get so upset at the kids! They are just kids. It's just, if Daniel is goofing off 30 percent of the time, and Joy is being defiant 30 percent of the time, and Michael is getting into trouble 30 percent of the time, on their own, they are being good kids 70 percent of the time. But all together…"

"That's 90 percent of your day!" Holly laughs.

"Exactly. It's exhausting."

"Do you ever get a break?" Holly asks.

"Um, break?" I think about that. "Well, I get to sleep. And sometimes I go grocery shopping by myself. And to the dentist. Do those count?"

"No," Mom says. "A real break. Doing something you like to do."

"Well, we went to the YMCA last week. I enjoyed that. It felt good to run again." I used to run all the time. "Come to think of it, I think it helps my stress level. I always feel happier after a run."

"All those endorphins." John is a runner too, when he has time, which is rarely.

"Could you go to the YMCA more often?" my mom takes a handful of popcorn.

"I guess, but I feel like a slacker. Like I should be doing school. Or I feel guilty for doing something for myself." My eyes fill up with tears.

"Isn't exercising and getting a break so you're a happier mother good for your kids? How is that selfish?" my mom asks gently.

Hmmm. Good point.

"You know what always helped me too, when I got stressed?" my mom says.

"What?" I sniffle and reach for a tissue.

"I tried to remember that there are very few emergencies. Dad always said that. I remember one time you girls weren't obeying, and we were late for church. I was getting impatient and saying, 'We'll be late for church!' and Dad just looked at me and said, 'Barb, church is not an emergency. So, we'll be late. It will go on without us.' Then he sat down and had a little talk with you two, and gave hugs and kisses, and we were late but it was fine. It didn't matter one bit."

I could picture Dad saying that in his West Texas drawl. He is so patient. When he used to take us fishing, he'd sit for hours in the boat with us, perfectly content to be on the lake with his daughters.

I think back to the Target episode. It sure felt like an emergency, but only because I made it into one. So what if I didn't get to Target that day? Life would go on. And so what if the chili didn't get made? We could have eaten pizza.

It's just hard to remember that in the moment.

*****

It's three days after Christmas, and my family has all gone home. I am on my bed with Daniel and Michael for Snuggle Time. John's cleaning up the kitchen. Joy fell asleep watching *Mary Poppins* and is tucked into bed already. We've started listening to books on CD in the dark at bedtime; the kids love getting to snuggle on Mom and Dad's bed and they listen better with the lights out. Tonight we're listening to *Farmer Boy* for the second time in a row.

Daniel is astonished and fascinated by this world of long ago: blacksnake whips, tin peddlers, fishing in the rain. These stories open a door into a hearty and thrilling world Daniel didn't know existed, a world where nine-year-old boys broke teams of oxen, stacked ice and fleeces, planted fields of crops, and learned to be men. Hearing about it seems to strengthen something inside Daniel. It's like he knows most of what kids are given today is fake; he can tell real when he hears it.

Daniel is sprawled out on the bed, his six-year-old body suddenly looking huge. I nurse Michael, kissing his bare baby foot as he gurgles his hilarious nursing gurgle "guh-guh-uh-uh-wogga-wogga" to himself. Snow has fallen in a deep blanket around our house, cozily tucking us in for the night.

We listen in on Father and Mother, Almanzo and Eliza Jane, Royal and Alice, all of them sitting around the cookstove, carving and knitting, eating popcorn and drinking apple cider. Daniel listens quietly and intently. This, from the boy who asked at dinner, "What if we put a rope in a coconut and lit it and threw it at the neighbor's house? On purpose?" On this cold winter's night in Oklahoma, my boys are utterly content with this story and with Mom. They are just as content as those Wilder children were, gathered in warmth with their family, on that cold winter's night in New York long ago.

"You guys sure are precious to me," I tell Daniel, looking into his eyes. "I'm so thankful God gave Daddy and me three darling children."

"I know, Mom," Daniel says, looking embarrassed but pleased. "Why do you always tell us that? We know!"

"I just want to make sure you always remember that. Even when you mess up or I mess up, I love you. Always. And God loves you always."

"I know, Mom," Daniel says, and rolls his eyes, trying to look like he doesn't care. Then he comes up and snuggles into me for a hug.

When I can relax, I remember: this is what my children need. This is what I need too. Snuggles, stories, the closeness of family. These small moments are the jewels that fill my mothering heart. Diamonds all around, moments of peace and sweetness.

I know these moments will fly by. This baby I'm nursing will be six soon, sprawled all over the bed. These baby feet I'm kissing will be all stinky and big. My six-year-old will soon be a teenager, no longer interested, probably, in reading with Mom.

The question about school is looming. Next week we'll have to make a decision. But tonight? Tonight I'm going to sit here on the bed and snuggle my children. School will come soon enough.

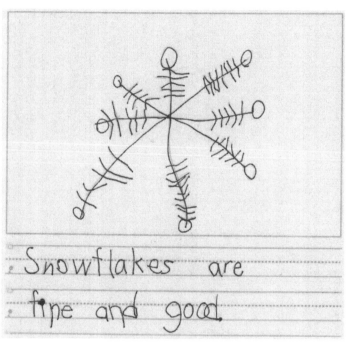

Snowflakes are fine and good.

Joy, 4 years old, magnifying glass observation of snowflake

Snowflakes are cool.

Daniel, 6 years old, equally effusive

# ~ January ~

Drat. Double drat.

It looks like God wants me to homeschool. How did this happen?

It's the day after New Year's, and I escaped to my favorite Thai restaurant, the one I always went to when I was pregnant, to read and think and pray. I got a fantastic curry and a Thai iced tea. I've spent the last two hours journaling and praying about our school decision.

*Ok, Lord, where do I start?* I prayed. *What am I supposed to do?*

I thought I would be looking forward to dropping Daniel off at Redbud Academy in the mornings. But somehow, I wasn't.

I wasn't really sure where to start. I opened my Bible to Psalm 128 since I love how that talks about families. I have prayed those words for our home and children before. I read:

> Your wife shall be like a fruitful vine
> In the very heart of your house,
> Your children like olive plants
> All around your table.

I've read that before. I've prayed that before. But today I noticed "in the very heart of your house." Hmm. My friends who have kids in school are in the car a lot. They have homework to supervise. The moms are stressed out and busy. They are not "in the heart of their house." They are in the car, running all over town. And they are tired. Like the women I used to work with. They all seemed worn thin.

Not that I was all that rested and fruitful myself. I felt worn thin too.

Then I read, "Your children like olive plants all around your table." The children are like little plants. And, they are learning and gathered around *my* table. Not the table in the school cafeteria. Rooted. Established. At their table. In their home.

Now, I know God might use those same verses to show some other mom something completely different. But what they said to my heart at that moment was: "Keep them home. Kids need roots. They need homes. They need families. Keep them home, while they are young."

I'll admit, I don't know what "young" is. I didn't look up the definition of "children." But, to me it means, you know, young. I'm not sure where that ends, but I know we're still there. I want my children to grow strong roots, so when they get out into the hot sun and fierce winds that are in this world they will be able to grow and thrive and bear fruit.

*Fine, so maybe I am called to keep them home. But, how? How do I do this? None of this has felt natural to me yet. I'm exhausted. What am I doing wrong?*

For some reason God brought to mind that verse about "all your children shall be taught by the Lord and great will be the peace of your children." I looked it up in my homeschool notebook. It is in Isaiah 54.

O you afflicted one,
Tossed with tempest, and not comforted,
Behold, I will lay your stones with colorful gems,
And lay your foundations with sapphires.
I will make your pinnacles of rubies,

Your gates of crystal,
And all your walls of precious stones.

**All your children shall be taught by the LORD,
And great shall be the peace of your children.**

In righteousness you shall be established;
You shall be far from oppression, for you shall not fear;
And from terror, for it shall not come near you …

"This is the heritage of the servants of the LORD,
And their righteousness is from Me,"
Says the LORD.

So, basically what I saw here was—a promise. That God would build this beautiful house. A palace, in fact, from the looks of it. Colorful gems, sapphires, rubies, crystals. Precious stones. Not unlike those mothering moments that fill my heart.

But, who is doing the laying of the foundation? God. Who is teaching the children? God. I think I need to let go of all my plans a little bit. They are obviously not working so well.

And the promise? That my children will have great peace. A heritage.

My job? Servant of the Lord. It seems like God is promising to do all this *in spite of me. Not because of me.*

So, looking back over all my notes in my journal, I'm not really sure what all that means yet. But I know two things. 1) God has laid it on my heart to keep my children at home with me for now and 2) He promises good things. I have to trust Him.

And you know, deep down, I think this is what I really want to do too. I think this is what's best for my children. I do know them better than a teacher would; I can give them focused and individualized attention.

John used to be on the Board of Directors for a private school in town for children with learning differences. Every year at the school's fundraiser I would hear the wonderful stories, but the main differences people mentioned were the low student/teacher ratio, the individual attention, and the teacher working with each child to help them learn.

What is a better student/teacher ratio than 3:1? I can work with Daniel to learn self-control and to focus, and I have more energy for it than a teacher would. Joy can enjoy being a little girl without worrying about having a boyfriend in fourth grade, as I remember doing. And Michael, well, he can play in the sandbox instead of riding around in his car seat all day picking people up and dropping people off. My children can learn to be who they are without the constant pressures of fitting in. They can play in the "forest" of the backyard, make tents in the living room, or lie on the trampoline and watch the clouds.

Though this homeschooling journey may be scary for me, aren't all new things? It will be an adventure, of the daily and quiet sort, but an adventure nonetheless. I'm thankful I don't have to work now, and I will have decades to work after my children are grown, but I don't want to miss these years because I was in a hurry. Or thought I needed to, in order to define myself. I want to focus on the job at hand; definitions will follow.

Deep down, this is the childhood I want to give my children: a slow waking up on the kitchen couch, watching the squirrel jump in the sycamore tree instead of us bustling off to school; long hours to build creations with blocks; or time to get out the watercolors, instead of preparing for the end-of-year test. Or for the next year. Or for college (as one school I visited proudly told me about their four-year-old class). College will come soon enough; they need time and space to be children.

And, you know, I want to be there with them as they discover this world and who they are, who God made them to be. I don't want to wake up one day and realize I missed it.

I want my children to have a childhood. And this is the best way I know to give it to them.

*****

After these revelations, I go home. I tell John what I think. He basically says, "Great! Sounds good to me." He is so agreeable. If I came home and said, "Honey, I think we should all fly to Kenya this summer, live in a hut, and help our missionary friends for two months," (which I actually *did* say the other day, come to think of it), he'd blink a few times, cock his head to the side and say, in a measured voice, "Really?"

John likes the idea of homeschooling, but only if I want to. He says he thinks I'll do a great job. I'm not sure why he thinks this, but he does.

After talking with John, I call Lisa. If I'm going to do this another semester, much less another year or two (or twelve), I need help. Seriously, how does she *do* this with seven kids? I need to know. She told me to come on over.

Michael takes a nap in the car, and Lisa's little ones have just awakened from their naps when we arrive, so everyone has a second wind. The kids go upstairs to play Star Wars, since it's freezing outside. Star Wars and dress up, combined. Nothing like a princess in tiara and high heels wielding a lightsaber.

The toddlers are shrieking and dashing around. One great thing about Lisa's kids is, they are so responsible; they are used to helping take care of each other. I know Michael is in good hands upstairs.

"How do you do it all?" I moan to Lisa, as we sit down at the kitchen table.

"Not very well, truthfully," Lisa smiles at me. "Life feels like chaos swirling around me most of the time."

"But your house is *clean!*" I say, looking around. Okay, not clean, exactly, but not covered in clutter as mine would surely be if I had seven kids. Her kitchen counters are clear. My counters usually have bowls with congealing oatmeal on them until dinner time. At least. Sometimes until the next day.

"That's because I'm obsessive about it," Lisa says. "I'm working on it."

"That's what all my clean friends say! I want to be obsessive too! Teach me!" I wish I could just transform into a clean person. Like on *Mary Poppins*. If I had a superpower, I think it might be that—the power to snap my fingers and clean a room. Or, snap my fingers and be nice to my children all the time. I'd take either one, really.

"No, it's not good," Lisa says with a sort of sad smile. "It comes from when my parents were passed out from overdosing, and I'd go around the next morning with these strangers asleep in my house, and I'd be cleaning up all around them. I felt like if I could clean up the house, everything would be okay, you know? By the time my parents woke up the house would be clean, and they'd be proud of me, and we could pretend everything was fine." Lisa had a really rough childhood. Just like Elizabeth, she's been through the fire. Now that they are Christians, they cling daily to God's grace.

"Now, when things are out-of-control, that's how I deal with it," Lisa says. "We stop everything and everyone cleans for a while. I'm not saying it's a good thing always, but it helps me. It's something God is healing in me, the hurt from all that." Lisa is so honest. I love that about her. No pretense.

"But let me tell you, I don't have it all together!" Lisa adds, laughing. "Have you noticed that the kids still have their pajamas on and it's now..." she consults her watch, "three o'clock in the afternoon? Our online bill paying was messed up, and I hadn't had time to fix it yet, so when we got back in town after Christmas we found out the water had been shut off. Oops. I'm hanging on by a thread, Julianne!"

"Me too!" I laugh. "That's exactly how I feel most days."

"But, I *have* been doing this longer than you, so maybe I've learned something that will help you. What is stressing you out the most?" Lisa asks.

I think for a minute. "Probably just the general chaos of everything. I feel like there are a hundred things to do at any one time. And I can't concentrate because Michael is always getting into something. It's exhausting."

"Okay." Lisa gets a notebook and pen. I can tell that as a former high school English teacher, she is relishing giving me an assignment. I'm starting to get a bit worried, truthfully.

"Write down all the things you have to do in a day other than school. Chores. Like, make breakfast, dress Michael, clean up the kitchen, stuff like that."

I write down my list. Lisa looks at it and starts circling things. "Okay, Daniel can sweep the floor. Or get a Dustbuster; that will change your life. They're like thirty dollars. So, Daniel can Dustbust after each meal. Joy can spray off the table and wipe it down. They both can help straighten up."

"It's just so much work to get them to help," I moan. "How do I get them to do it?"

"Just say, 'You are part of this family and we all have work to do. Mommy's work is making the meal. Your work is helping clean up after the meal.' You'll be surprised—they sort of like it. They like having a job and a responsibility."

"So I don't need to pay them?" I ask.

"Noooo." Lisa shakes her head. "They have jobs to do because they are part of the family. If they want to eat that meal, they need to do their job. Or if they want to watch TV or play outside or whatever. Those are privileges, not rights. And, I've noticed they appreciate their play time if they don't get to play all day. They have work to do. This pays off big time in school too, because they are used to having to work hard and obey Mom. They don't get all bent out of shape because they think math is interrupting their play time.

"My kids have to pick up their room and put their laundry away, as part of their responsibility of taking care of their things and being part of the family. However, I will pay them for extra chores, like vacuuming the living room. That way they get practice saving, giving, and spending."

"Okay, that makes sense," I agree. "I do think they are old enough to do that; I just get tired of thinking of who should do what and when."

"Well, that's why you're going to make a chore system," Lisa tells me. "Right now. I'm going to go make some coffee. While I do that, you write down all your weekly chores. Put all the stuff on there that should be done, even if it never gets done now. You want to have a time for that so it doesn't create stress."

"Like getting and sorting the mail," I say. "I just pile it in a basket and ignore it until John deals with it. But I know it's there."

"Right," Lisa says. "Like that. Now, if you don't care if it's done, like washing the windows or something, leave it off. Just put the stuff on there that you'd really like to be done."

I work on my list while she works in the kitchen. She comes back with hot coffee and Girl Scout cookies. Bless her.

"Done!" I show her.

"Great!" She looks it over. "Now, go back through and assign things to people. Who can do what? Other than you. Your name should only be next to the things that you have to do, like get Michael dressed or make dinner.

"Oh, also," she adds, "you could have the kids pick up the house twice a day. Before lunch and before dinner. Clutter equals stress. Each thing out of its home creates a decision that has to be made or a task that must be done. The kids need to keep their toys in their homes."

That reminds me of what Vanessa told me about everything having a home. Up until now I had been the one putting the things in their homes, but I like the idea of the kids doing it much better.

"Sarah, can you change Levi's diaper please?" Lisa calls. "Okay, Julianne, you work on that; I'm going to make a phone call."

Off she goes again. I am beginning to learn part of her system—delegating. I didn't know she was going to make *me* do all the work here.

Lisa's oldest daughter, Sarah, wanders by, presumably looking for her brother. Her head is bent forward over her pink phone. She is texting away, giggling to herself.

Oh no, not her too! Do all teenage girls sprout pink phones attached to their thumbs when they turn thirteen? No, it's probably even younger now; I'm always behind. It's probably when they're ten now. Or eight.

Only three more years until Joy is sullenly slouching at the dinner table grunting at me while she shovels peas in her mouth, her eyes darting to her phone on the counter. I know how these things work; I've read *The Winter of Our Disconnect*. I know how these talkative children grow into wired teenagers, barely deigning to interact with their poor, backward moms anymore.

We need to travel back in time and live like the Wilders in *Farmer Boy*. Those kids didn't need iPhones to entertain them.

You know what would be even better? We'll move to a remote Swedish island—they probably don't even have Internet access over there. We'll skip around on the rocks and hike through the forests together. We'll sing Swedish songs and make pepparkakor cookies at Christmas, like Pippi Longstocking. And now that Tiger Woods' ex-wife moved out to one of those islands with her children, my kids can play with some other Americans, until they learn how to speak Swedish. John could get a job as an accountant specializing in fishing exports or whatever they do there.

It's the only logical solution.

"Jules?" Lisa's voice breaks into my thoughts. "How's it going?"

"Huh? Oh...um...great!" I start working on my chore list again. It takes me a while because after I assign things, I put the jobs in order.

Lisa comes in and looks over my shoulder at my list. "That looks good."

"Okay, but I have a bunch of questions!" I say. "What do I do about cleaning chemicals? I have Daniel cleaning the kids' bathroom, but I don't want him using bleach or anything."

"We use spray bottles filled with half water, half vinegar," Lisa says. "The vinegar works great as a natural cleaner anyway, and it's safe if they, you know, drink it. Or spray someone in the face. Or whatever. It might sting, but it's not going to burn their eyes out, you know?

"Then for the tub I have them use baking soda," Lisa goes on. " Works as well as Ajax. I have Sarah do the toilet, but when the kids were little I did it—too many gross germs to have little ones doing it."

"Right. I can just see my kids using the toilet brush as a lightsaber." I shudder.

"Ugh. I know. Plus the toilet is the one place where I do use strong chemicals, so that's a big person job. But when the little kids are wiping the counters and faucets, I have them use baby wipes," Lisa says. "It works. Gets all the gunk off."

"What about mirrors?" I ask.

"The vinegar spray. I've read all these complicated recipes for natural cleaners, but I can't keep them straight. I just dump in some water and some vinegar in a spray bottle, and it works. In the kitchen I do water with a few drops of lavender essential oil. It smells great and lavender is a natural disinfectant."

"Okay, but…" I feel like I'm arguing, but I am still confused. "I've sort of tried this before, and I can't keep track of it. How do I make sure we actually do it?"

"Well, I'm so glad you asked!" Lisa beams at me. "You need a 'Super Duper Chore Keeper!'" She pulls out a nametag holder, the kind with the little silver clippy on it.

"That's what we call them anyway," Lisa laughs, "to make them sound extra exciting. I think technically they're called Chore Packs™. They came with this book, *Managers of Their Chores*. What I do is get some index cards and cut them in half. Then I have one card for each chore. You can start with the Saturday ones, since the daily ones are pretty simple. I use blue cards for Weekly Chores and yellow for the Daily Chores. So, on a blue card here in the middle you'll write the chore name, like "Clean Your Room" and at the top "Daniel." For Joy, you could draw a picture or not—she's probably old enough to start reading the words, plus, it's good reading practice. Then you put all the cards in the plastic holder, and they clip it to their belt or shirt. As they complete one chore, they move that card to the back, and so on."

"Aah, so no more forgetting what they are supposed to be doing!" I say. "That's brilliant!"

"Oh, they'll still forget," Lisa assures me. "You'll be training them in these and reminding them what they're supposed to be doing for months. But they'll learn quickly, especially if they don't get to play until chores are done. They get really fast at it."

"I love this!" I tell her. "I feel like it's taking some of the responsibility off of me constantly directing people, and putting it on them."

"Exactly." Lisa nods. "It's one less thing for you to think about. All the decisions have already been made. So it frees your mind up for other things. Like what to make for dinner."

"Or maybe something more fun." I can be hopeful. "Like the book I'm reading."

"Oh, yes. Definitely for that. Hey, I got this great book from the library the other day. It's a mystery set in England with this feisty—"

"Um, Lisa?" I hate to break in, but if she starts telling me about a book, we could be here for hours. "Can you tell me about it when we're done?"

"Oh, right, sorry. Okay, so anyway, be tough; don't feel mean for making them do this work. They need to learn to pick up after themselves. And, it makes them a whole lot less likely to make a mess if they know they'll have to clean it up. They are going to have homes and families someday. They need to know how to be responsible for their own things and chip in to be part of the family. You can be very nice about it, but firm."

"In fact," Lisa goes on, "when I used to teach, the kids thought the whole world revolved around them. They could hardly believe they were expected to do *anything*; they were outraged about it. Part of our jobs as mothers, whether we homeschool or not, is to prepare our kids for life. These really are practical skills that they need to know. Plus, you're teaching them to be considerate instead of expecting you to serve them all the time."

"Yes!" I say, "They can be so demanding! I feel like I'm being ordered around by three irrational little people all day. They expect me to do things for them all the time. They make messes wherever they go, with no awareness of it. It's totally irritating. I think this would help a lot."

"I do too," Lisa says, "but don't be surprised if it doesn't work perfectly. This is just a place to start. You may have to change the system, or use something completely different. The main idea is that *it's important to have the kids help you. You can't do it all yourself.* Here you go." She hands me the scissors.

"Now?" I ask. I was hoping for some more Girl Scout cookies and a break.

"Now," Lisa says firmly, "you need to have this done when you leave here. I'm going to see if the kids have collected the eggs. " Lisa has six chickens and some goats. Her house is as good as the zoo.

Man, she is a slave driver, though. But, that's what I need. I need to get tough. Here I go.

I make out all the chore cards. It didn't even take as long as I thought. I put them into the little name tag holders Lisa gave me: one for me, one for Joy, one for Daniel, and one for John, so they can see Daddy has chores too. John is about to start his busy season at work, so he won't even be there on Saturdays, but in April we'll have him back. I decided Michael doesn't need a chore keeper yet.

I finish that and go upstairs to look for Lisa. The boys are up there playing Star Wars LEGOs on the computer. (I let the kids play video games at their friends' houses.) The girls are playing "Baby Monkey Chunk" which seems to involve one of them being the mommy monkey and the others being the baby monkeys and making monkey sounds. And also, inexplicably, bocking like chickens. The babies are content to be surrounded by the chaos.

I see Lisa coming down the hall. "Okay, I'm done. And my head hurts. Can we stop now?"

She laughs. "No. Not yet." Is she kidding? How much more can we say about chores? "We need to talk about how you're going to get a break."

Oh, that! I'll happily discuss that. We go back downstairs; I sit in the kitchen and chop carrots and talk to her while she starts dinner.

By the time we leave I feel good. I have a plan.

*****

On the way home I take the kids to Sonic. I order seven corn dogs (the kids eat two each), two bananas, orange juice for them and Diet Coke with vanilla for me. The kids peel all the breading off the corn dogs, so it's really a hot dog on a stick that I pay a dollar for but, hey, at least I don't have to make it or clean it up.

I know feeding my children corn dogs is terrible. I know this. I'm going to fix it right after I Become an Organized Person and Learn How to Homeschool Successfully (Without Losing My Ever-Loving Mind). Become a Healthy Mom. It's on the list. I can only do so much at a time.

This is why I only read like a few verses a day in the Bible, and that's on a good day. I take a while to process things. So, if I'm learning about being at peace with all people (especially those little ones) and not letting a root of bitterness spring up, that could take me like a year to implement. I'm working on it. I'm not ready to move on yet.

I did order bananas, though, so that makes a balanced meal, right? And orange juice! That makes two fruits! And, when we sit at Sonic and wait for our order we play Sonic math, which is my own little invention, so we're doing school too. I'm really good at schooling them when everyone's strapped down.

"Okay, Daniel, here's a question for you," I look in the rear-view mirror at him. "Our order cost thirteen dollars and thirty-four cents. I have a ten, three ones, a quarter, and a dime. How much change should they give me?"

"A hundred dollars!" Joy shouts.

"Joy, this is not your question. This is Daniel's." I look in the mirror and see his face screwed up, thinking.

"A ten, and three ones…" Daniel mutters to himself, "and a quarter… okay that makes twenty-five cents… and a dime…thirty-five… how much did it cost again?"

"Thirteen dollars and thirty-four cents."

"Okay, then they should give you… one cent change!" he yells excitedly.

"Very good, Daniel!" I tell him with a smile. "Excellent! Okay, Joy, this one's for you. One quarter is the same as how many pennies?"

"A dollar!" Joy yells. She is so precious. She just wants to be as big as Daniel and randomly yells out whatever comes to her mind.

"No, less than that. A dollar is one hundred pennies. A quarter is worth…twenty…."

"Five!" Joy screams. "Twenty-five pennies!"

"Yay! You got it right! Great job, Joy!"

Joy is beaming. "That was so *easy*. Ask me another one."

"Okay, how many pennies does a dime equal?" I ask.

"Twenty-five!" she declares confidently.

"Well, no, a *quarter* is twenty-five, remember? A *dime* is as many as the number of fingers and toes you have. How many fingers and toes do you have?"

"Ten!"

" Yes! A dime is the same as ten pennies! Great job, Joy!" I smile at her in the mirror. She grins back.

"Okay, Michael, your turn," I say to Michael, who is watching us with interest. "If you had five baby toes and five more baby toes, how many baby toes would you have?" Joy looks at Daniel with an "Is Mommy crazy?" expression on her face.

Michael looks at me and smiles.

"Bah!" he says and points to the ball on the floor.

"Yes! Ten baby toes you'd have! Michael, you're a baby genius!" I say, and reach down to get his ball. The kids laugh.

"You're a baby genius! You're a baby genius!" Daniel repeats, ruffling Michael's hair.

Our food arrives; I pay and dole out the hot dogs on sticks and juice. I turn on the radio to listen to while we eat.

I hear a piece on the radio about the protests in Cairo and ask the kids who knows what continent Egypt is on. Daniel knows, of course, and we have a good discussion about Egypt, Joseph, Moses and Pharaoh's Quest LEGOs. I try to point out that Pharaoh's Quest isn't actually real, and there aren't such things as flying mummies, but I'm not sure Daniel believes me.

Then, Daniel starts telling Joy all about the wolf guardians and his latest LEGO magazine, and the teachable moment is gone. Oh, well. At least we can learn about Egypt without weaving papyrus from river reeds. Maybe next year.

We're doing more and more school this way, in two-minute conversations as we go about our days. It doesn't make a nice, neat spreadsheet, and I forget to write most of it down. But I know the kids are learning. They are learning about money at Sonic, about x-rays and bones at the doctor's office, and about democracy when they come with me to vote. There are a thousand lessons to learn all day long, when we simply slow down enough to pay attention.

A lot of learning happens smack-dab in the middle of life, it turns out.

## Daily Chores

"Morning chores" – potty, clothes, brush teeth, make bed, brush hair
"Evening chores" – potty, brush, rinse, floss, wash faces
Meal Clean Up Chores - Daniel/Joy alternate months
Floor duty (Dustbuster)
Table duty (spray off)
Ten-minute Tidy – everyone helps clean up living room and dining room

## Weekly Chores
### Wednesdays (mandatory)
Trash Duty – Daniel (empty all trash cans)
Laundry Train – Joy (take all laundry to laundry room)
### Saturdays
### Mandatory
Pick up your room
Put away your clean laundry
Vacuum your room
### Optional (earn from .50 cents to $3 each, depending on size of chore)
Sweep and mop kitchen and laundry room – Julianne
Clean up all clutter in kitchen – Julianne
Go through mail and file papers – Julianne
Clean kids' bathroom – Daniel
Vacuum living room, dining room, hallway – Daniel
Water plants – Joy
Vacuum entry way – Joy
Shake out bathroom rug outside – Joy
Help Mommy – Michael
Mow lawn, outside chores, bills, balance checkbook – John

## Phase I – Changes for Julianne to make
### (meet with Lisa in one month to discuss)

1. Train and help kids with new chore system (work on cheerful attitudes)
2. Go to YMCA at least 2x/week
3. Find a babysitter to take kids for a whole day 1x/month
4. Don't worry about school for two weeks. Get house running smoothly.
5. If extra time, can read or do some school if we feel like it.

# ~ February ~

This morning we are on the way to co-op. I can't wait to talk to Lisa. Her family was sick, then ours was sick, so this is the first time we'll both be at co-op in weeks. I want to tell her—having the kids do chores is the best thing ever. What took me so long to do this?

I think I got behind when Daniel was born, and I never caught up. I've been behind for like seven years. I finally feel as though we're on top of things. The house is clean! It's been clean for three whole weeks. I love it!

I didn't realize how much stress the clutter was causing. The kids had forts in the living room, puzzles in progress on the dining room table, and toys scattered about. Lisa's brilliant advice to limit the kids to one project at a time has helped tremendously. The laundry used to pile up in disheveled heaps, but now the kids pitch in, and we're doing much better at getting clothes washed and put away.

(A friend recently asked me if I fold the clothes or if I have the kids fold them. "Folding? What is this *folding* of which you speak?" I'm lucky if I can get the clothes sorted, and the kids to lay them flat in their drawers. Daniel's interpretation of "lay them flat" is "ball them up and shove them in the drawer until it's so full you can barely cram it shut" but, oh well. The clothes are put away, and I don't care if they're wrinkled. Maybe someday we'll work on folding, but I honestly can't imagine it. It's such an implausible and irrelevant luxury, like worrying about whether I should choose a wood or an aluminum yacht; I'm still trying to keep my canoe afloat.)

Joy is in the back seat screaming at the top of her lungs along with her CD, "I'm a three-toed, triple-eyed, double-jointed dinosaur with warts up and down my back! I love shiny autoMObiles, tow trucks and airplanes, and I like to munch on railroad tracks!" She pauses and asks Daniel, "What are autoMObiles?"

"Carts," Daniel replies, with authority. "AutoMObiles are shopping carts."

"Actually," I clear my throat, "automobiles are cars. Like the kind you drive."

"Oh, right—cars." Daniel says, as though that's what he meant to say the whole time. He is pretty sure that he has learned about everything he needs to know during his long life on this earth, despite my attempts to instill humility in him. I think this unfounded but benign arrogance is a common trait among first-graders, though. A few months ago, I was guest-teaching in his co-op class and for fun, I asked the kids, "Who thinks your teacher knows more than you?" and the kids looked around at each other, smiling politely, waiting for the next question. I think two out of twelve kids raised their hands.

We arrive at co-op, get out of the car, and load up our stroller with diaper bag, co-op bag, a costume for Daniel's history skit, snacks for Joy's class, and finally, Michael. I get Joy and Daniel settled in their classes and join the moms in the baby nursery for the first hour.

My other homeschool support group has a broad range of political and religious viewpoints among its members; some of them homeschool for religious reasons, some social, some academic. While I appreciate the wisdom and ideas in both groups, there's something special about this group of co-op moms here at church. Not only are they my kindred spirits in this world of homeschooling, they are precious sisters in Christ.

I probably *could* homeschool without them, but it wouldn't be nearly as much fun.

Lisa rocks a baby while Sabrina changes a toddler's diaper. One of our fellow co-op moms, Keisha, is filling in for Elizabeth today.

"How's Elizabeth doing?" I ask Sabrina. She is dressed in black pants, a red shirt with ruffles around the neck, and black *heels*. And she's wearing lipstick. (I am wearing exercise pants and a fleece jacket.) She always looks so together, but she tells me that in Colombia women just dress up more.

"She's...let's see...I think she's about thirty-one weeks along." Sabrina tells me in her beautiful accent. "She's had high blood pressure, off and on for the last month, and lots of mild contractions. Her doctor put her on complete bed rest until the end of the pregnancy."

"*Giiirl*, I don't know how she's doin' it," Keisha exclaims. "Bed rest? Seven months pregnant and three kids to take care of? Lord knows, I'd be at the end of my rope."

"I know!" Sabrina answers, smiling. "But she's had a lot of help. Her mom visited over the holidays, then her sister came and stayed with them in January. I put a sign-up out in the foyer for some of us co-op moms to take shifts to help her. We need to pray she makes it until March. Thankfully their insurance would cover another NICU stay, but she's hoping to avoid it."

"How are the babies doing?" Lisa looks concerned.

"Actually, they are doing really well. They aren't going to find out the genders, but they know that Baby A is over three pounds, and Baby B is almost four. Praise God for that!"

That sounds so tiny, but I know it's good for twins. And there is still a month to go for the babies to gain weight.

"I need to sign up to help her," I say, sort of to myself, as I finish off my third peanut-butter oatmeal cookie. Things have been going so much better at home that I feel like I can give a few days to help someone else. "Okay, Keisha, these cookies are awesome!"

"Oh, I know," Keisha says, her chocolate eyes laughing. "I had to get them out of the house or Darren and I were gonna make ourselves sick. But, just so you know, they aren't my *signature* dish. They are good, but they're not my *signature* dish."

"What's your signature dish?" Lisa asks.

"Well, now, I haven't decided yet. But I know this ain't it," Keisha says with attitude, and we all crack up.

"How's it going with you, Julianne?" Lisa asks me.

"Oh, my goodness, so much better. The kids are doing their meal clean up chores—they seem to love having their own responsibilities—and I feel like I can breathe again. I'm not always one step behind them. Now, after meals, we all clean up together, and when the kitchen's clean, we can go sit on the couch and read. Normally, I would finish in the kitchen, only to find three other messes they made while I was busy. I'm not sure how long this will last, but I hope it's permanent."

"I need to get Sophie doing some chores," Sabrina says thoughtfully. "She *is* seven. It just seems easier to do it myself sometimes."

"Yeah, but the side benefit is, she will help with everything more." I am now a big advocate of chores. "The kids have suddenly become aware of the world around them. Daniel saw Michael throwing Cheerios off the high chair the other day and said, 'Hey, Michael. No throw! I just cleaned that floor.' It was awesome."

"Wow!" Sabrina says. "That's what I need. Sophie thinks she can put things everywhere, and it's my job to clean up after her. But what if she only does the job halfway? I'm pretty picky."

We turn and look at Lisa, our Chore Guru. "Well," Lisa says, "you need to train them to do the job well. If I'm teaching Grace to spray the table after meals, for example, I'll give her three lessons."

"Grace is only three years old!" I say in surprise. "You have her spray off the table?"

"Sure. She can do it. So, I'll give her three lessons. In the first lesson, I show her how. 'See Grace, get the spray out from under the sink. Then you spray, but not on the wall, not your brother, not yourself, see? Just the table. Then you get one paper towel. One. Not the whole roll. And you wipe off the table.' Lisa pantomimes wiping off the table. 'And then you throw the paper towel away. Then you put the spray under the sink like this.' I tell her every detail.

"The second time, she tries it herself, and I coach her. The third time, she does it by herself, and I watch and inspect at the end and give her lots of praise. After that she's on her own; I just check in periodically. And I do remember she's only three. The job won't be done perfectly, and that's okay."

"That seems like so much work!" Sabrina sounds like me now. "Do I have to do a sticker chart or something?"

"I don't," I said, looking at Lisa. Lisa and I hadn't really talked about stickers, but I don't have energy to keep up with that. "And you're right Sabrina, it was work for me to train them, but it's already paying off."

"Okay, I'll try it." Sabrina has a determined look in her dark eyes. "I've *got* to get Sophie helping more. Did you know we're trying to adopt?"

"No!" I hadn't heard that. "When?"

"Not sure. We have to raise money first—we're still in that stage. I'm babysitting some neighbor girls once a week and trying to think of some other things I could do."

I suddenly have an idea. "Hey! Would you want to watch my kids for a day once a month? I was going to get a babysitter, but I'd rather have them go to your house. You could put the money toward your adoption, plus it would be nice to have the kids out of the house. That way I could do a massive cooking project or something."

"Or take an exercise class," Lisa reminds me, "or go to a nice restaurant and read and journal. You're supposed to do something fun and relaxing for yourself on those days, remember?"

"Oh, yeah. Right." Another thought suddenly strikes me. "And you could teach the kids Spanish! I've been wanting them to practice the Spanish they are learning in co-op." Sabrina's daughter has grown up hearing English and Spanish and is fluent in both. "I'm sure they'd pick it up. Ooh, plus, if you teach them Spanish, I could count it as school. Will you think about it?"

"I will, but I think I'd love it!" Sabrina smiles at me as she picks up a toddler and sits down to read him a book. "Your kids are great, and Sophie gets lonely being an only child. She'd love to have the company."

"Hey, how's John's job going?" Lisa asks. I had told her about the tension at his work lately.

"Not well. He had to lay off two employees a few weeks ago. One of the guys has four kids; we're praying that he'll find another job soon. John hates this part of his job. He's got to find more clients soon, or he'll have to do more layoffs." I try not to show that I'm worried, and I don't mention John getting laid off, but my friends seem to have a radar about these things.

"Ladies, sounds like we've got a lot to pray for," Keisha says. "Let's do an open-eyed prayer right now."

"Absolutely," Lisa agrees. We glance around to make sure everything's peaceful in the nursery, then, with our eyes still on the munchkins toddling about, we pray.

*****

It's a cozy Thursday evening; a fire dances in the fireplace, and outside huge snowflakes drift from the darkening indigo sky. John's busy audit season is in full swing, so he is still at the office tonight. He's been working even more than usual to try to bring in new jobs, as well as to make sure his current projects are on time and under budget.

The kids and I are snuggled up on the couch with a pile of winter books, working our way through our library book basket. They are in their clean clothes, ready for bed. Here's the thing: we don't do pajamas. At least, Daniel and Joy don't. And here's the really big news: it doesn't matter. We've all survived quite well, surprisingly.

Back when Daniel was a toddler I thought, "What's the point? You put pajamas on at night and then take them right off again in the morning." Jammies added one more step in the excruciatingly lengthy bedtime routine. It was enough we had to brush their teeth every blasted night. I kept saying to John, "Can't we outsource this? They should have mobile tooth brushers who come to your house every night and do this for you. I'd pay for that!" But alas, no one came to help us out, so we had to do it ourselves.

Okay, it also took forever because we were clueless parents and followed those ridiculous ideas in parenting magazines about negotiating with your two-year-old: "Do you want to brush Mommy's teeth?" and "Look, here's a new spinning toothbrush!" and, "Oooh, you opened your mouth tonight; here's a sticker! Hooray!" Please. Now we say to Michael, "Open your mouth, buddy; it's time to brush your teeth." If he says, "No!" we put him in his crib, and he cries for two minutes and then decides to open his mouth. Why don't they tell you *that* in a parenting magazine?

I do put Michael in pajamas, but mostly because they're so stinkin' cute. Tonight he is sitting on the floor with his red-striped reindeer pajamas. He has crammed his feet into Joy's high-heeled pink dress-up shoes, because a) he's obsessed with trying on all of our shoes and b) he likes the clippety-clip sound they make on the wooden kitchen floor. He's sitting on the floor playing with a tiny soccer ball, and the kids are taking turns reading with me. Occasionally he gets mad that someone else is sitting in Mommy's lap and wails his loud, outraged cry, but I ignore him, and he gets over it. Then he comes up to read with us. He gets a turn in my lap too, but not every turn.

Now, cozy on the couch in front of the fire, we've read an illustrated *Stopping by Woods on a Snowy Evening* by Robert Frost, *Gingerbread Baby* and *The Mitten* by Jan Brett, and *Snow* by Uri Shulevitz. It's Michael's turn now, and I read him his favorite, *Ten Little Ladybugs*. He doesn't understand the concept of winter books anyway.

We were at Elizabeth's today, to "serve Jesus by serving Elizabeth." The kids played really well with Elizabeth's kids while I cleaned up and made dinner. After being in a tiny house with six kids all afternoon, our house feels incredibly tranquil by comparison.

It's funny—I remember thinking I'd never be able to help other people if my kids weren't in school during the day. Now, I'm realizing that we all get to serve together. My children are with me when we take someone a meal or babysit for a friend. What better way for my children to learn to serve than by serving with me, like the disciples did with Jesus? I realize I'm not Jesus, but I am called to teach them God's truths when I sit in our house, when I walk by the way, when I do laundry, and when I make dinner. Or something like that.

I finish reading to Michael, and he wanders off to look at an ornament on the Christmas tree. Even though it's February, the Christmas tree is still up in the corner. Daniel and Joy weren't ready to take it down yet, and neither was I. It still feels like winter, and winter needs twinkly lights. This is how Christmas should be anyway, all quiet and peaceful. Everything was cancelled last week because of snow, so we happily stayed home.

We talked about pints, quarts, and gallons, and glued pictures onto construction paper to make a measurement chart. We made cinnamon rolls and discussed fractions and tablespoons, cups and degrees. Michael is old enough now to involve him a bit so he doesn't feel ignored. He had a great time rolling out and smushing the dough on his highchair tray.

Daniel sits down next to me, and we start to read *The Jacket I'll Wear in the Snow*. Out of the corner of my eye, I notice Joy playing with a fuzzy wind-up bunny left over from her Easter basket. She winds it up, and she and Michael watch it hop along the hearth (actually, it's more of a slow hobble—the bunny has lived a long and full rabbit life). I'm halfway listening to her as I read to Daniel.

"This is my pet rabbit. I'm going to let him out of the cage and he's going to go really fast!" Joy is such a cute storyteller. Michael happily watches her animated face. "There were lots of bunnies, and this one gotsd scratched and bled, and this one gotsd scratched and bled, and this one gotsd scratched and bled. So they all died. This one's the only one left. Hop, hop, hop!"

What??? Where did that come from? You'd think we let her sit around and watch *Friday the 13th*! It's like a chipper bunny version of some horror movie: lots of scratching, blood, and hopping bunnies.

She cheerfully winds up the rabbit and sets him off again for a smiling Michael, who is blissfully unaware of the macabre and bloody plotline in his furry friend's life.

Sometimes I tune in to something my kids have been saying and think, "What? Hold on; rewind." And I mentally go back in the conversation I've been ignoring and realize the weirdness has been going on for some time. It's like several parallel universes. My mind seems to be right here in reality, while theirs are shooting off in various bizarre, and totally unrelated, directions. I never really know where they are coming from and where they are going—sort of like we've all been tessered and are on some temporary, strange planet in a tiny person's version of *A Wrinkle in Time.*

Daniel does this all the time—surprises me with some announcement—and I have to figure out where he's coming from and where he's going, and more importantly, am I going to let him go there? This morning, for example, Daniel's first words to me as he walked into the kitchen were not "Good morning," but, "I know something we can do in the fall when it's windy!"

"What?" I asked, reaching out cautiously, like a person who's not sure if she wants to get dragged along by a passing truck.

"We can make a parachute and jump off the fort! With a sheet!"

He sounded so certain of the brilliance of this idea that I sort of hated to mention little details like gravity. And perhaps, broken bones. I had to decide over hot tea and eggs—was I going to let them proceed with this plan: the dragging of sheets to the backyard, the plummeting to the ground? But then, I realized, they probably wouldn't actually break a leg; it's not that far down to the ground. And it's possible, albeit unlikely, that Daniel would forget about this idea by next fall. So I opted to say, "Oh, well, that's an idea!" and tried not to sound too exhausted.

I hate to stifle his creativity, but he comes up with complicated and physically voluminous ideas at an astonishing rate. It wears me out. In the car the other day, out of the blue, it was, "Mom, I'm gonna need some big bricks."

"Really, why?"

"To build a pyramid."

"Where are you planning to build it?"

"In the backyard. That way we can get the sand out of the sandbox and put it all around and it will be like the desert."

I should totally say no. I get that. But I secretly admire his initiative. I mean, what confidence! No hesitation, no question of whether or not he could do it, or the pesky issue of *how* to build a pyramid, just, "Mom, I'm gonna need some big bricks." That's kind of awesome.

On that day though, I was tired to start with, and after a lengthy discussion on geometry and architecture and patio logistics, I thought of the answer I should always give: "Great idea, Daniel! But you need to ask Daddy."

Tonight he is relatively placid though, contentedly listening to me read. I let Joy and Michael keep playing with the rabbit because it keeps them quiet. I read a few pages of our current chapter book, *Hudson Taylor*. It's a tremendous story of faith, and there's a picture on every page to keep Daniel (and usually Joy) interested.

The phone rings. I try to ignore it, but when I hear Elizabeth's voice on the machine, I pick up.

"Hey, Jules. I wanted to let you know—the boys found General Grievous's head." Elizabeth laughs.

"Whew! Daniel will be relieved. He was in the depths of despair." Daniel insists on carrying miniature LEGO figures with him wherever he goes, despite my warnings that he's going to lose something. Maybe he'll listen to me next time. "Hey, how are your contractions?"

"Better. I'm bored to death, but the contractions have slowed." When we were over there this afternoon, she was sitting up talking to us, and she started to have mild contractions again. I sent her to her room with strict instructions to lie down and watch TV.

"Good!" I encourage her. "Only three more weeks to go. You can do it! Hey, I should bring you some audio books on CD. I'll see what I can find at the library tomorrow."

"That would be awesome. Love you, friend."

"Love you too. Good night."

I round up the kids, who by now are wrestling on the floor; we brush teeth and sing Family Song. (We're still singing "Go Tell it on the Mountain" from December. I haven't gotten around to changing it.) I tuck them in and kiss them goodnight.

I go to the kitchen and load the dishwasher. The kids helped me clean up the table earlier, but I still have some dishes left and counters to clean. I don't really feel like it; I want to continue reading *Little Women* in my room. (It's a long book! It takes a while since I only read about five pages a day!) But it's so nice to wake up and come out into a bright, clean kitchen. I'm willing to tidy up for five minutes while my tea kettle heats up on the stove.

As I wipe off the counter, I think of something I read by Charlotte Mason, an eighteenth-century educator. She wrote that the mother who teaches her children good habits "secures for herself smooth and easy days." I see the truth in that. It reminds me of the verse in Hebrews about how "no discipline is pleasant at the time, rather painful." However, I am beginning to see the "harvest of righteousness and peace" this habit training is producing, both in my life and my children's.

The tea kettle whistles, and I pour the steaming water over my decaf tea bag. I notice the new schedule I have taped up on the clean and de-cluttered fridge. It's quite different from the one I had in September. There are fewer activities on the schedule, but we do them more consistently. I feel like if we get those basics in (meals, Bible, snuggles, and chores) the rest of the day falls into place. Sort of like Lisa was telling me back at the convention, I realize. I guess I just had to figure out what our family's basics were for myself.

John's mom asked me if I'm planning to give Daniel a standardized test at the end of the year. She even thoughtfully sent me a newspaper article about how the U.S. lags three years behind China in math and science, and a year behind Finland and Korea in reading. Perhaps that was her way of reminding me to cover those subjects. She's so nervous about the whole homeschooling thing, like the kids will be twenty, and I'll slap my forehead and say, "Oh, math. Right. I forgot about math!"

I considered giving Daniel a test, but Oklahoma doesn't require it, and it would add stress, preparation time, and expense. And frankly, I know my child better than a test does. A test won't measure if Daniel can actually think (the newspaper article even mentioned that). It won't gauge honesty or kindness or self-control. And it's difficult to weigh the contents of a child's heart. We sat on the couch tonight reading about Hudson Taylor, a man who changed the world with his faith and courage and integrity. None of that would have shown up on a standardized test. So, how Daniel would do on a test really isn't the point. He's learning truth and virtue, perseverance and character, to love God and to follow Him wherever He may lead. Those are the most important things.

I add some half-and-half to my tea and notice the poem hanging on the wall by our breakfast table. I had to relocate our art and poetry study to the kitchen since we never go up to the schoolroom any more. Our artist study for this month is Georgia O'Keeffe.

Next to the bold paintings of mountains, sky, desert bones, and flowers is taped this poem:

### Barter, by Sara Teasdale

Life has loveliness to sell,
All beautiful and splendid things,
Blue waves whitened on a cliff,
Soaring fire that sways and sings,
And children's faces looking up
Holding wonder like a cup.

Life has loveliness to sell,
Music like a curve of gold,
Scent of pine trees in the rain,
Eyes that love you, arms that hold,
And for your spirit's still delight,
Holy thoughts that star the night.

Spend all you have for loveliness,
Buy it and never count the cost;
For one white singing hour of peace
Count many a year of strife well lost,
And for a breath of ecstasy
Give all you have been, or could be.

The poem says it well. Homeschooling (like life) is barter. There's a tradeoff. There is strife, and there is a cost. But, the lovely things are worth it. The beautiful things aren't easy. There will be times of crying, of praying for patience, of frustration, but there are also hours on the couch with my children, pouring truth and beauty into their souls. To me, it's worth the cost.

*Eyes that love you, arms that hold,* indeed.

I take my mug of tea, turn off the light, and go to bed.

# ~ March ~

Oh, finally! Blessed sunshine! Even though it's only the first week of March, Tulsa is having a warm spell. Daniel made me a sweet card this morning because he knows how much I love spring. The kids and I are out in the backyard today enjoying being out of the cave, I mean, house.

"Buh!" Michael says, pointing a pudgy finger at the cardinal chirping in the neighbor's pecan tree.

"That's right, buddy, that's a bird!" Joy says, smiling into his chubby face. She is such a sweet big sister to him.

"Okay, Mommy, close your eyes!" Joy instructs me. I comply.

A few minutes later she comes up: "Okay, open them!" Joy is holding out a bouquet of yellow, blossoming branches from the forsythia bush.

"They're for you, Mommy!" Joy beams at me, her brown eyes sparkling in the sun.

"Oh, honey, I love them!" I kiss her upturned face. "Thank you! You are such a kind little sweetie!" She runs off to play in her playhouse with Michael.

I can't believe Joy is five already! We had her birthday party a few weeks ago. A few of her friends came over, and we baked zucchini chocolate-chip bread. They are all so precious, those girls—so tiny, but so fierce and funny. I want them to stay that way forever.

Today Joy is dressed in a long, flowery skirt, a sweater with snowflakes on it, purple Crocs, and a cowboy hat. A silver tiara is perched atop her cowboy hat. Because cowboys often need tiaras, out on the range. I keep asking her if she's getting hot, but she's determined to wear that sweater.

Daniel is on the patio setting up army men. We are having a Civil War History Week, so I got my dad's plastic army men out of the attic. This morning Daniel and Joy colored little paper flags and taped them to popsicle sticks: one Union flag, one Confederate.

Daniel was supposed to be Ulysses S. Grant, and Joy was supposed to be Robert E. Lee, but Joy kept messing up Daniel's soldiers.

"Joy, you are the Confederacy! These are Union soldiers! Yours are the black ones," Daniel tells her. She keeps forgetting, or purposely ignoring him, I'm not sure which.

"Joy, if you can't leave my soldiers alone, I am going to banish you from the battlefield," Daniel says sternly.

Joy thinks for a minute. "What's 'banish' mean?"

"It means leave forever and not come back." Daniel is standing with arms crossed. Joy decides to go gather wildflowers (actually, weeds) and stops listening.

Daniel keeps talking, "That's what 'banish' means, Joy. So." He pauses a beat. "Am I going to have to banish you or not?"

"Hey, Daniel, let's be kind to your sister, please," I say to him in a soft voice. "I don't think she wants to play anymore anyway, so you can do all the soldiers yourself."

"Whew!" Daniel relaxes a bit and goes back to setting up the blue soldiers. But then Michael starts running on his chubby baby legs over to the battle scene.

"Michael, no!" Daniel yells. "Mom, Michael is going to destroy my soldiers! Get him!"

"Okay," I say, "but calm down, please. It's okay. Try not to yell."

"Okay," Daniel says, trying to calm himself down. He's made great strides this year in self-control, but I can understand the frustration of people always smashing up your stuff. I can't believe it—one more week and Daniel will be seven. Seven! It seems so big! He's lost his first top front tooth, and his gappy smile makes him look both vulnerable and grown up, all at the same time.

I intercept Michael mid-run and swoop him up. I fly him over and plunk him in the baby swing.

"Here you go, baby." I push Michael in the swing and quote Robert Louis Stevenson, as usual: "How do you like to go *up* in a swing / *Up* in the air so blue?"

"Up! Up!" Michael laughs and claps gleefully, as he whooshes back and forth in the swing.

"Buh!" Michael says, and points his plump finger at the white butterfly flying by.

"Buh-ter-fly!" Joy tells him clearly. "Yes, Michael! That's a butterfly!"

"Buh!" Michael says. He thinks it's a bird. Oh, well.

"No! Butterfly!" Joy says to him.

"Buh!" Michael insists.

"Okay, buddy," Joy says, laughing. "You can call it a bird."

"Hey, Joy, can you push Michael for a few minutes? I'm going to go put these flowers in water."

"*Oh, sure!*" Joy loves to take care of Michael, though he gets a bit worried sometimes. That's something I really love about homeschooling—the kids are home all day with their baby brother. They adore him and he adores them. Maybe I'm wrong, but I don't think they'd be as close if they only saw each other a few hours a day.

I go inside to put the flowers in water, then come back out with a copy of *The Old Schoolhouse* magazine to read as the kids play. And also, the *Pottery Barn Kids* catalog, just for fun.

"Mom, which side won at the Battle of Gettysburg?" Daniel is all about accuracy.

"I can't remember; what did that book say?" I ask him.

Daniel goes in the house and comes back with *Just a Few Words, Mr. Lincoln.* "Okay, this says the Union won."

"Great." I am so proud of Daniel. He has worked really hard this year, despite the general chaos and disorganization.

Things are much better than at the beginning of the year though. And now that the house is running more smoothly and things are generally clean and non-overwhelming, Lisa came over and helped me find ways to get a little more school in.

The first thing Lisa suggested was to have Daniel work independently more often since he can read now. He's been reading a chapter of an easy reader book during his rest time, then after his nap he narrates back to me what he read. Also during his rest time I have him do a math speed drill, just practicing the addition and subtraction facts we've already covered. After he does these two things, he is free to play LEGOs.

The other change Lisa suggested was to do workbook lessons (spelling, reading or math) during Michael's nap time, instead of reading during that time. The first hour of Michael's nap is rest time/quiet time for everyone, including me. Then the second hour I do lessons with Daniel (and Joy, if Joy is still awake). School is so much less stressful when we do it during Michael's nap time. We all cry a lot less.

To make up that reading time I cut out, Lisa recommended books on CD from the library. We listen to those as we drive to the YMCA or Joy listens at rest time. If it's an easy enough book Joy follows along with the words so it's extra reading practice for her. They've listened to *Tikki Tikki Tembo, Leo the Late Bloomer, Amelia Bedelia, The Composer is Dead, Click Clack Moo, Little House on the Prairie, Mr. Popper's Penguins,* and lots of others. Plus, John reads to the children at bedtime, and I read to them randomly throughout the day, so they still get lots of snuggle reading in.

We actually are not too far behind my plan at this point, although even that phrase bothers me. Who says we're behind, and why I am using "their" standard? My kids are learning and growing, and that's what really matters.

We *were* five weeks "behind" in spelling, so we did a Spelling Extravaganza week, where we did one spelling list each day instead of each week. Daniel spelled out words while jumping on the trampoline, holding up index cards, building the words with LEGOs (one letter on each LEGO) and hopping on root words and suffixes drawn in chalk on the patio. Joy got to do the games with us for reading practice, and she helped read out the words for each day's spelling test. She is doing great with her reading—she can sound out almost all the words in her Awana Cubbie book each week.

This week, however, all we are doing is history.

We've made a cookie map of the U.S. and colored in the north and south states with frosting (an idea I got from that curriculum at the homeschool convention). The kids all *loved* that of course. Daniel built a replica of a plantation with LEGOs and Play-Doh. We read books and watched movies about Abraham Lincoln, Harriet Tubman, and John Newton (who helped end the slave trade in Britain). We listened to CDs of slave lullabies and made dried apple rings. It has been a wonderful week. Tomorrow I'm hoping to have the kids do a collage, trace a map for their history notebook, and put some pictures of Abraham Lincoln and Harriet Tubman on the history timeline, along with the dates of the Civil War.

Another thing that is so awesome is that Michael has been playing independently more. The other day we were up in the schoolroom, and he was sticking plastic tools in his tool bench, then taking them out, over and over. He did that for maybe *fifteen minutes*. Fifteen minutes is an eternity in my life. If Michael can be occupied with something for fifteen minutes, that gives me hope for next year.

I look over at our raised garden bed. I paid some neighborhood boys to till the soil for me last week, so the weeds are gone and it's ready for planting. You know, it's a nice day—we might as well put in this year's garden.

"Hey guys, want to plant our garden?"

"Yeah!" Joy abandons Michael in the swing and runs to the shed for her plastic tools and tiny Dora gardening gloves.

"No, thanks." Daniel is engrossed in the Battle of Gettysburg on the patio.

"Okay, Joy and Michael, you can help me." I lift Michael out of the swing, then get the seed packets from inside. I show Joy how to make a row in the dirt, then sprinkle some seeds in and gently cover them up with dirt. Michael sits at the other end of the garden and digs a hole, merrily flinging chunks of soil over his shoulder.

I have a friend who would freak out if she saw this—I'm not making Joy follow the suggested spacing for seeds; she's just scattering them in. I figure we'll thin out the plants later. My friend knows the planting dates and spacing of every seed, how to amend her soil, and the intricacies of composting. But last year? She got so overwhelmed by the whole thing that she didn't even plant a garden. If she couldn't do it perfectly, she didn't want to try.

Joy finishes up her crooked row of radish seeds, then plants a few rows of spinach, arugula, and beans. (I think it's late enough to plant beans; we'll find out.) I show Joy how to write "radishes" on a popsicle stick with a Sharpie, and she stabs the stick into the dirt at the end of each row. She marks each row until half our little garden is planted. We stop here for today.

My expert-gardener friend will buy her produce at the farmer's market or the grocery store this year, and it will look better and taste fine. It's certainly more predictable. But nothing can compare with the excitement I saw on Joy's face last year when she saw the radishes *she* planted smiling up at her through the dirt like hidden rubies. She planted, she watered, and God brought the increase. Her face held wonder like a cup; her eyes were shining pools of amazement and delight. You don't get that from a science textbook.

Our ragamuffin garden never goes according to plan. I make elaborate sketches of neat vegetable rows that are forgotten as soon as the kids and I are out, boots on, digging in the dirt. I forget to weed. Sometimes I forget to water; sometimes the kids water too much. Occasionally, bunnies get the lettuce. And every year, despite my floundering, or maybe because of it, I learn something new.

Homeschooling is a lot like my garden. It's messy. My method seems haphazard. I am learning as I go. It rarely turns out exactly like I planned and the results are unpredictable. At some point along the way, I feel like a failure. But somehow the roots go down deep; the tender plants grow strong. And every single spring, every single summer, I am awed by the harvest God brings.

I wash our hands off with the hose and go inside to make hot dogs for lunch. For myself, I make a green smoothie with leftover baby spinach. I have to hand it to my sister on this one: these green smoothies are the fastest, easiest, healthiest lunches ever. The kids even drink some, so they get vegetables and don't even know it.

I get everyone all settled at the tiny picnic table outside. Joy prays, and we start to eat.

Daniel thinks of a joke, "What is a dog with a fever called?"

I can guess the answer but play dumb, "I don't know, what?"

"A *hot* dog! Get it?" Daniel starts cracking up and so does Joy.

"Okay, I have one!" Joy says. "When does the horse cry to the cow?"

"I don't know." I am genuinely puzzled about this one.

"In the afternoon! Get it?" Joy starts laughing uproariously.

"Joy, that doesn't make any sense." Daniel looks confused.

"Yes it *does!*" Joy insists. "In the after*noon!* The after*noon!*" Is she thinking "noon" rhymes with "moo" so that's the joke? I have no idea. Daniel and I look at each other and start laughing because she's so adorable.

Michael is laughing too, though he has no idea why.

This is another thing I love about homeschooling—leisurely days with my children. Despite the addition of curriculum and lesson planning, and the fact of being around children all the time, I think homeschooling really is a simpler life.

When Daniel was in a Mother's Day Out program briefly, I remember he'd be involved in some meaningful, creative, wonderful play and I'd have to rush him through breakfast, into the car, into his coat, to the school, just to pick him up, rush him through lunch and to naptime, while having no real idea of what he did all morning. Now I get to spend slow hours with my children—planting a garden, discussing battles, enjoying them—and they get that unhurried childhood time that they wouldn't get if they were in a classroom all day. Yes, the actual school part can be hard—the math lessons, the spelling test, keeping the baby busy—but I don't think the overall lifestyle can be beat. Homeschooling is turning out to be a simpler, slower, richer life.

"Okay, I'm thinking of a country," I say to them. They love these guessing games and don't realize they're learning something.

"China!" Daniel knows the countries from the Risk board, so he's got pretty good guesses.

"Nope."

"Arizona!" Joy screams excitedly.

"Nope. That's actually not a country, but good guess," I encourage her. "Here's a hint, it has a cold climate and is an island."

"Mexico!" Joy is sure she's got it.

"No, good guess!"

"Greenland!" Daniel yells.

"Nope, but so close!" I say.

"Ooh, I know—Iceland!" Daniel gets it. Iceland is on the Risk board. It's an unfair advantage, really.

"Yes, great guessing guys!" I encourage them.

Joy pouts, "I *never* get to go to Iceland." As if we all went there last week and left her at home.

"Maybe someday we will," I say. I really think we should travel the world at least a *little*. Assuming the accounting business picks up, my husband keeps his job, and we ever have any extra money again, that is.

I actually have been to Iceland (in college) and know this: the kids would love Iceland. We could travel the Ring Road, see geysers and waterfalls, swim in the steamy Blue Lagoon, and go on a boat trip among the glaciers. Ooh, and puffins. Michael would love the puffins ...

My cell phone rings.

"Hey, Elizabeth," I answer, looking at the display.

"Actually, it's Steve," I hear Elizabeth's husband say, "Elizabeth wanted me to call you. She had the babies!"

"What? Really? Are they okay?"

"Yep. Just two days shy of being full-term. They're girls, and we're naming them Charlotte and Caroline. Charlotte's pulse ox levels are a little low, but they've got her on oxygen and the doctor says it's nothing to worry about. They probably will be released when Elizabeth is, so they should go home with us. We are so thankful; thank you for all your prayers."

"Of course," I say, with a lump in my throat. "Oh, Praise the Lord. I want to see those baby girls!"

"Elizabeth knew you would," Steve laughs. "I have to relieve the babysitter at home in a few hours. She's wondering if I can watch your kids, so you can go up to the hospital to keep her company for a bit. She's requesting that you bring a decaf caramel macchiato."

"Man, I'll bring her whatever she wants. She just delivered twins!"

"Okay, great. Thanks, Jules. I'll see you tonight."

"Okay, bye Steve. And congratulations!"

"Hey, guys!" I say to the kids when I get off the phone. "Guess what? Elizabeth just had her twins! They are healthy and perfect! Two little girls; they named them Charlotte and Caroline."

"Can we go see them?" Joy asks. Then she adds, "Actually, Mommy, no one's perfect except Jesus." Great, is she going to start correcting me now that she's five?

"True," I tell her. "But babies are pretty close. You guys can see them in a few days, absolutely."

"Beh-beh!" Michael says. He adores babies. He looks like such a big guy next to them now.

"I wish I had twin sisters!" Joy pouts again.

"Me too!" Daniel says.

"Yes, well. We can just be excited for them," I say, briskly. "Rest time!"

The kids take their paper plates to the trash and go lie down for their rests. I try to figure out what I could take over to Elizabeth's house for dinner. As I'm staring into the freezer for inspiration, the phone rings again. It's Ginger, calling to talk to me about the surprise party for Frank and Vicky in May.

"I just wanted to be sure you guys have your hotel reservations and everything," Ginger bubbles. "I guess that's graduation weekend at SMU so hotels are filling up fast. I've heard the club is booked solid, so good thing we're having the party at our house." The club is Dallas Country Club. "Our party is Sunday night, though, so almost everyone we've asked can come! It's going to be fabulous!"

"Of course it will be," I tell Ginger warmly. "I'll go make our reservations right now. I'll call you back and let you know where we're staying."

" 'Kay! Bye!" Ginger is positively giddy.

I go to the computer to look up hotels in the Highland Park area. Well, perhaps we'll stay a little farther out, so we don't have to get a second mortgage on the house to pay for it.

The whole idea of this party is making me nervous. I don't like parties anyway, talking to a bunch of people I don't know. I *really* don't like talking to a bunch of rich, well-behaved people I don't know when I've got my rambunctious and very loud children with me. You know that rule I have about staying as far away from polite society as possible? This is totally breaking it. My kids have to get through dinner and a speech without humiliating John, his parents, or me. I shudder, remembering the elevator button incident in California. They are such darling children, but they have a special knack for embarrassing me. I'm starting to sweat just thinking about it.

Also, the last time I spoke to her, Ginger told me John's grandmother is going to attend the party. Great.

John's grandmother is one of those opinionated elderly people that loves to say whatever is on her mind. We saw her at Christmas when I was pregnant with Joy. She looked me up and down and said, "How much weight have you *gained*?" I was so surprised I couldn't think of a good answer so I meekly said, "Forty pounds?" Her jaw dropped and she gasped, "That *much*? I can't believe it! They only let us gain fifteen when *we* had babies." It was lovely. Such an encouraging visit.

When she found out we were homeschooling she said, "I can't *believe* people don't even let their children go to *school*. Terrible." I see where Vicky gets it.

I know that I don't *have* to prove anything to them, but I still *feel* like I do—at least that the children aren't completely anti-social and illiterate. I know God is the ultimate judge, but I just want John's family to think I'm doing a good job; I can't help it. Is that so wrong?

The other issue with John's grandmother is that she's a complete stickler for manners. She expects children to say "yes, ma'am" and "yes, sir" and carry on polite conversations. Lately, Daniel and Joy have been completely ignoring adults at church who are trying to engage them in conversation. Getting eye contact and a mumbled "thank you" out of them, much less anything that resembles polite conversation, is like pulling teeth. We better start practicing.

And here's the other issue: Dave and Ginger have a big pool in their backyard. The last time we were at a fancy graduation party at a mansion in Tulsa, Daniel fell into the fishpond. Thankfully, he can swim, but Joy and Michael can't. I will need to keep them with me at all times.

Just add it to the list of potential disasters at this party: badly behaved children, intense humiliation, and, also, death by drowning.

Can I just enjoy the thought of getting ready for a fancy party? No, no I cannot. I will try my best, really, just as soon as I figure out what I'm going to wear (Do I own a fancy dress anymore? And if I do, will it fit?) and what we're going to get for Frank and Vicky's gift (Dave and Ginger got them a cruise).

Right after I figure out the dress/gift situation, and think of some ways to avoid an unfortunate falling-into-the-pool incident, oh, and practice manners with the kids, right after that, I'm going to get excited about this party.

| | 2010/2011 School Schedule – **Revised (Again)** | |
|---|---|---|
| 7:15 | Julianne wakes, showers, gets ready, breakfast, Quiet Time | |
| 8:00 | Breakfast, clean up chores | |
| 9:00 | Bible time on the couch, singing and hugs | |
| | Walk outside & snack (Joy/Michael) / Daniel – plays LEGOs inside | |
| | *SCHOOL – some kind of game or project or read a book; kitchen or upstairs* | |
| 11:30 | Lunch, clean-up chores | |
| | *SCHOOL – read a few books* | |
| 2:00 | Rest time (nap for Michael) | *(Daniel SCHOOL – does reading/speed drill, then plays LEGOs)* |
| | *SCHOOL– (while Michael's still asleep). Workbook/lessons.* | |
| | Play outside – all *OR go to YMCA* | |
| 5:00 | Ten-minute tidy before dinner | |
| 5:30 | Dinner, clean-up chores | |
| | *READ/PLAY – John working late; read a few books (If Mom has energy; if not – play or watch a movie.)* | |
| 7:30 | Evening Chores (brush, floss, etc.) | |
| 8:00 | Reading & Family Song | |
| 8:30 | Lights Out | |

# ~ April ~

We are actually getting something done this morning—Praise the Lord!

We have been venturing up into the schoolroom again, and it's going so much better. I think part of it is that I have lowered my expectations. A lot. If we get one thing done, that's an accomplishment. No longer do I try to squeeze twenty-seven activities into the morning.

Today we were late waking up, and late eating breakfast. (We had spaghetti for breakfast; it's a long story.) We were late doing Bible time. (I can't seem to find a children's Bible I like; it's another long story.) We finally made it upstairs around 10:30. The kids are always surprised when we go up there. "We're doing school today?" they ask. But I understand the confusion since our schedule seems to change weekly. I'm working on it.

So, we are upstairs this morning. I got Daniel seated at the antique wooden desk, and he's started on his spelling lesson. Joy is working on the first page of the A Beka kindergarten phonics book. I had ordered it for next year, but she keeps begging to do it, so I'm going to let her start. She's picked up a lot of reading with practicing letters and blending them together to make words, but I want her to have a good phonics foundation.

Then I sit down to read Michael a book. I've learned that I'm much less impatient if I am doing something else while the kids are working. Sometimes if I'm looking over their shoulders I get all impatient, all "Hello? 2+2? How hard is that?" inside my head and feel my entire life floating right past me as I sit here doing first-grade math. Things are better when I have something else to do. Then I can just verbally check in with the kids every few minutes or when I see them staring off into space.

I read to Michael, "Fish! See the fish? Let's count the fish..." and use his index finger to count all the fish on the page. Michael is very happy if he has Mommy's undivided attention.

"Mom, what am I supposed to do here?" Joy needs help on the next page.

"Bring it over here, please. Let me see." I look at the page. "Oh, they want you to circle everything that starts with the short i sound. So, ih-ih-insect. And you circle it. But eh-eh-elephant. Does that start with ih?"

"No way!" Joy shakes her head emphatically. "So I won't circle it."

"Right. Good job, Joy!" She runs back over to her table to do some more.

"Daniel, how's it going over there?" This is my way of helping Daniel focus without saying "Daniel, stop staring at the wall and do your spelling, please."

"Oh! Good, Mom." Daniel busily starts working on his spelling again. He is doing so great today; he hasn't whined yet.

I go downstairs to make a copy of a covered wagon picture from a book so we can stick it on our history timeline. I should really do all this preparation ahead of time, but whatever. Maybe next year I'll prepare in advance. I can always dream. As I finish reducing the wagon to make it teeny tiny, I hear Daniel saying, "Mom, help! I'm being attacked by a baby!"

I dash back upstairs to find Michael climbing over the top of Daniel's desk, sitting on his spelling book, and squashing Daniel in a big bear hug.

"Ow-sigh! Bah-ket-bah! Shoot!" Michael is saying.

"No, Michael, we can't go outside and play basketball right now!" Daniel laughs at him. "Mom, argh, he's choking me." Michael has been going to Daniel lately if I don't give him what he wants. It doesn't usually work, but he figures it's worth a shot.

"Michael, stop attacking your brother. Sorry Daniel, that does make it a little hard to do your work, doesn't it?"

"Yeah, but it's okay." Daniel loves it when Michael mauls him. He adores being a big brother.

"Come here. Let's go read." I pry Michael off of Daniel and take him back over to the couch. "Look, *The Wheels on the Bus!*" We read that, picking out all the animals and people in the pictures. Joy runs over to ask me about a picture in her workbook every now and then. In twenty minutes, Daniel and Joy are finished! Daniel got his entire spelling worksheet for the week done, and I don't think I ever heard a complaint. Joy wants to keep going in her workbook, but I make her stop so we can put things on the timeline.

I give Joy a tiny picture of an Acoma Pueblo ceramic pot to tape on the timeline, and show her where to put it. (We read about the Southwest because we were reading about the Santa Fe wagon trail. The Acoma Pueblo Indians had been there for a thousand years already, apparently, so we had to go way back on our timeline to add the pot.)

I ask Daniel to cut out the tiny wagon picture I just copied while we do that. He finishes and I put a tape circle on the back (I can't find my double-stick tape) and ask him to think about where it goes on the timeline.

"Hmm, let me think…" he says, pondering the timeline. "It would be after Jesus, and after the Mayflower and the Declaration of Independence…"

"Right!" I tell him. "That's exactly how to think about it. Ooh, okay, think about what that big purchase of land was called, when Jefferson bought that land? What was that called?"

I notice Michael is over by the fiction bookcase pulling books off the shelves. "Michael. No touch! No touch books."

Michael looks at me, smiles, and tosses some more to the ground.

"Okay, I told you 'No Touch.' Sorry." I pick Michael up and put him in his little gated-off area. Since he hates it anyway, I decided just to use that for his Time Out area when he doesn't obey. We've been working on "No Touch" lately. I can't have him flinging everything to the floor and causing chaos and destruction.

Daniel is trying to ignore Michael's screams while thinking about what Jefferson's big purchase of land was called.

"The Purchase of Louisiana?" he finally remembers.

"Yes! Good! The Louisiana Purchase! So, look on the timeline and see if you can find that."

Daniel finds it and sees the date: 1803. "Okay, so it was after that, right?"

"Yes, because first Lewis and Clark and Sacajawea had to explore it, then later other people started coming in wagons. Very good thinking, buddy! That's the way to figure it out." I show him an open spot, close to where we have a picture of Laura Ingalls Wilder taped up. "How about here? It's actually anywhere along here; wagon trains went west for years." Daniel tapes up the wagon.

"Do you know why the wagon trains stopped?" I ask him, trying to ignore Michael's sobs. I'll get him out in a minute.

"Um... cars?" Daniel guesses.

"That's a very good guess! It's something like cars. Something that went fast like cars that replaced the wagons."

"Tractors?" he guesses again.

"No, but you're super-close. We drew it on the map, remember?" I show him in our history notebook where he and Joy had traced the wagon trails and the Intercontinental Railroad in colored pencil.

"Oh! The railroad!" Daniel realizes, the light going on in his eyes.

"Yes! The railroad! Excellent! See, when the railroad went through, people could just get on here..." I show him on the map, "... and zip right out west. So they didn't need to use wagons anymore. Great job, Daniel."

"Mommy! Michael's climbing out!" Joy screams at me.

"Okay, I'll get him." I go over and scoop up Michael, who somehow has climbed over the gate and is sliding headfirst toward the floor.

I get a tissue and wipe off Michael's tear-stained face.

"Michael, Mommy said 'No Touch' and you didn't obey," I tell him soberly, pointing to the bookcase. "Can you say sorry?"

Michael pats his chest, the sign we made up for "I'm sorry."

"Can you give Mama a kiss?" I ask. He gives me a kiss on the cheek.

"Okay, are you ready to obey Mama?" I ask him. He nods his head. "Oh-beh."

"Good boy." I give him a hug and kiss. "Now, let's go pick up these books." We go over to the bookcase, and I have him help me pick up the books he threw down and put them back on the shelf. I was at the park the other day and another lady asked how old Michael was. When I told her that he was almost two she said, "Wow, he's so smart! You can tell he really understands what you're saying! I have a niece who's almost three and she doesn't listen to her mom at all."

"Well," I told her, as nicely as I could, "we've worked a lot more with him than I did with my other two. I didn't think they could understand, but now I realize they really can. They understand way more than I thought." I decided not to say, "Um, is it possible your niece understands exactly what her mom is saying, she just doesn't want to listen?"

"Can you guys pick up your animals, please, and clean up?" I instruct Daniel and Joy. "We're done for today."

"Yay!" Daniel and Joy exclaim and happily gather up their stuffed animals. I've been letting them bring their stuffed animals to school; apparently animals need an education too.

We've only been up in the schoolroom forty-five minutes, but we've done short lessons in spelling, phonics, and history. We will do more during Michael's nap time, Lord willing. I'm learning to stop when we're ahead, before people have meltdowns.

Michael's maximum attention span in any one area is about an hour. He was in his high chair in the kitchen for about an hour for breakfast and clean up time. We moved to the living room for Bible time on the couch with singing and snuggles; Michael alternately sat with us and played with a balloon and an animal puzzle. I think he's now reached his limit in the schoolroom. A walk would do us all good. Even though we just go down the street and back, with Michael in the stroller and the kids on their bikes, it calms us all down. We love our outside time.

*****

"Mama, am I almost six?" Joy asks me. We are in the car going on a field trip.

"Well, not quite," I say. Her birthday was in February.

"Am I almost five and a half?"

"Well, you're..." I do the math, "...five and a quarter."

"Oh." Joy sits quietly for a few minutes. "And Daniel is seven and a nickel."

What is she talking about? Oh! "Oh, sorry, I meant five and a *quarter of a year*. Not quarter of a *dollar*."

"Oh, oh," Joy laughs ruefully at herself, shaking her head, "I just get mixed up sometimes. Quarter of a *year*. Got it."

It's tricky business, this figuring out of words. Joy hears a word and thinks she knows how to use it, and it's so heartbreakingly precious I can't bear to correct her. Lately it's been "recognize." "Mama, do you recognize we're almost out of milk?" "No, I didn't recognize that, thank you!"

I'm glad the whole quarter thing is at least concrete and easy to explain, unlike their favorite topic of late—heaven. They keep asking me complex questions as I drive down the road. Michael will be "reading" *The Very Hungry Caterpillar* to himself: "Lollipop! Big! Fat! Buh-tuh-fly!" and then his favorite page, "Big! Fat!" over and over again. Joy will be interrogating me about heaven: "Are there girl angels too, or just boy?" (I don't know). "Will I be able to fly too?" (I don't know; maybe?). "Will I be there forever?" (Yes). "Is it imaginary?" (No). "Will that frog we saw get squished by the car be there?" (I don't think so). "Why will the frog not be there?" (I don't know). And so on, and so on, and so on.

I'm glad for their interest in spiritual things, I am, and I should go research the answers. But sometimes it's nice to not have an eschatological discussion as I drink my morning coffee.

"Okay, guys, how are we going to act at the sheep farm?" I ask them. "Are we going to run around and scream?"

"No!" they shout.

"We're going to be quiet!" Daniel says, from the third row of our SUV.

"And, we're going to listen!" Joy says, from the second row.

"Yes! Exactly right!" I say. "We're going to listen to Mommy and our tour guides, right?"

"Yes, and we're going to stand on our heads, right?" Daniel adds. "And throw our baby up in the air and catch him, right?" Sigh. Can we not have normal conversations like normal humans?

"Daniel, when Mommy is talking, I want you to answer respectfully," I say as Daniel and Joy crack up. "It's not time to be silly when Mommy is giving you instructions."

"Oh, sorry, Mom," Daniel says.

"Thank you, sweetie. When I give you an instruction, I want you to say, 'Yes, Mom,' okay?" I get so tired of making them repeat this twelve thousand times a day, but the alternative is they ignore me, which means I repeat myself twelve thousand times anyway.

"Okay. I mean, 'Yes, Mom,'" Daniel says, nicely this time.

"Thank you. Okay, you guys can listen to your CD now!" I turn the Classical Advantage CD back on. Daniel and Joy quickly put their headphones on and start singing: "Remember the ladies, they were strong and brave too! Abigail Adams was First Lady number two. Dolley Madison was First Lady number four. She saved things from the fire during the 1812 War!" I know Joy has no idea what that means, but she is having a good ol' time singing it. And the best part is—since all the rhymes are on CD, I don't have to do anything to teach it to them. It just soaks right in. I guess there are some good things about the Classical method after all. Not that I'll be teaching my children Latin anytime soon. But this part is easy enough.

We arrive at the Shepherd's Cross sheep farm just in time to see a yellow school bus pull up. We are meeting Vanessa and her kids at a working sheep farm near Claremore, Oklahoma. Vanessa's kids are on a class field trip, and I decided we'd tag along. The farm is midway between our houses, about an hour's drive for each of us. The school kids burst out of the bus, followed by teachers and moms. I give Vanessa a big hug. I haven't seen her since that day at the sprinkler park on Riverside last summer, the day of Joy's Spectacular Salvation Army Meltdown.

The kids all gather in a group to listen to their teacher's instructions. Vanessa and I hang out in the back of the group. Vanessa looks like Gwyneth on a Farm, naturally. She's wearing jeans, boots, and a cowboy hat. She looks amazing. And me, well, at least I am not wearing exercise pants. That's an improvement.

Sabrina is always telling me I should dress up more. "You're so pretty!" Sabrina said to me last week when I picked up the kids from her house. "You need to wear clothes that fit! What is it with Americans and exercise pants? And put on some makeup!" Ugh. I hate makeup. I am doing my best to wear at least mascara and lip-gloss. And brush my hair.

Vanessa's twins are up with the group along with Daniel and Joy. I'm holding Michael who keeps pointing at the sheep and declaring "Bah-Bah!"

The kids' teacher is going over the same things we talked about in the car: not yelling, walking, listening to the tour guides. Vanessa and I are far enough back that no one can hear our whispering.

"How is all the organizing going?" Vanessa whispers. "Are you now the World's Most Organized Mom?"

"Oh, hardly." I roll my eyes. "But it's a million times better. My friend, Lisa, helped me get a chore system going, and the kids are helping a lot more. Last week we were making resurrection rolls for Easter and the counter was covered in cinnamon and sugar. Joy said 'Mommy, can I wipe off the counter for you?' And Daniel said, 'Can I clean the floor for you, Mommy?' I about fell over."

"That's *amazing!*" Vanessa whispers back.

We have to be quiet now because the shepherd is starting to lead the tour. The shepherd is a real veterinarian who goes by "Dr. D." She leads groups on tours of her farm. She talks about how often the Bible mentions sheep and shepherds. Vanessa told me this was an optional field trip since her kids go to public school and the farm has a definite Christian focus. A few children opted to stay at school and do a different activity.

"The sheep know the shepherd's voice. They won't listen to other voices. They listen for my voice like we listen for the voice of the Good Shepherd," Dr. D. says. We've been here several times, and she is always so gentle and good with kids. I want to be as gentle as she is.

"Here in this pasture are our baby lambs," Dr. D. tells the children. She explains how the mothers are very protective of them. "This one is our bottle baby." She shows how the workers feed the lamb with the bottle and instructs the children to be very quiet. The children all get a chance to pet the lamb. It is so soft and sweet! Michael stands with his arm around the lamb, barely taller than it is, like it's his best buddy. I wish I had brought my camera.

We follow along as the shepherd explains how the sheep eat grass, how they naturally "fertilize" the fields and how they are Jacob's sheep, like in the Bible. Joy comes to show me she has sheep poop on her pink kitty-cat boots.

"Oh, well," I say. "We'll clean it off later."

"What a good mother you are," Dr. D. says to me. That is so nice! She does make me feel like a good mother. She points out the pond and reminds the children of how Psalm 23 says, "He makes me to lie down beside still waters."

"Hey, I know that verse!" Daniel tells her, as he walks beside her. "Want me to say the whole chapter?"

"Sure," she says, "You can tell me while we walk over to the Bible garden."

Daniel skips along beside her saying, "The Lord is my Shepherd; I shall not want." He quotes the whole thing, word perfectly. *Thank you, Lord. I have no greater joy than to know that my children walk in the truth.*

"Wow!" Dr. D. says to him, then smiles at me. "That's so great! What a joy to hear those little voices saying God's Word."

"Well, it's not me. They are in an Awana Bible Club at church," I say honestly. "I wouldn't have the discipline to do that on my own, but they work through their little books and learn their verses. They love it."

Another guide now leads the kids through the Bible garden, telling them about the different herbs and plants. I have to make Daniel hold my hand, because he and Vanessa's son keep running ahead and playing. He's embarrassed to hold my hand, but I tell him, "I'm sorry, you need to stick with me for a while because it seems like you're having trouble being quiet and listening." When he finally calms down, I let go.

Then the children go into the barn and learn about shearing wool, cleaning it, carding it, and spinning it into yarn. Michael keeps squirming and trying to run away, so we're both glad when the tour is over. We all get our sack lunches and sit down at the wooden picnic tables on the lawn. I finally can set Michael down, and he runs all over the yard, delighted to be free.

He keeps going over to another one of the moms with a baby and saying, "Beh-beh!" He points to me as if to show me his find: "Beh-beh!"

"I see, buddy, I see!" I tell him.

Daniel and Joy eat grapes, cheese, and leftover Matzo (unleavened bread, like a yummy flat cracker) from Passover. We are Christians, but we do a simple Passover seder—it's so rich with tradition and meaning. In fact, on the tour, the shepherd mentioned how Jesus is called our Passover Lamb and was crucified on the exact same day and hour as the traditional Passover lamb.

After lunch the kids have some chocolate Easter eggs, then run off to tumble around on the grass. Vanessa and I are left to finish our lunches in peace. The older school kids are taking a knitting class in the barn, so the younger kids get to stay outside and play for a while.

"How's John's work going?" Vanessa knows what's been going on from our occasional phone calls.

"Oh, a little better." I sigh. "At least he hasn't lost any more clients. He doesn't have any new ones though. He's working all the time." I realize that sounds like complaining. "I mean, I'm glad he has a job, don't get me wrong. I just miss him during busy season. It makes me so thankful that he's not in the military or something. At least with his job, it's only for a season."

"Yeah, I don't know how single parents do it. They are amazing." Vanessa agrees. "Hey," she says suddenly, "Eric's brother was saying the other day that his bank is doing some government program, and it looks like they are required to have an audit. Would John want to drive all the way out there?" Vanessa's husband is a cattle rancher, but his brother lives in a small town nearby and is an officer at a bank.

"Sure! He drives all around the state to other jobs. I think he'd love to have the work, and it's close enough that he or his staff could drive up in the morning and back at night. Will you email me his phone number and stuff?"

"Of course. If I don't, remind me, okay?" Vanessa gazes out at the blue sky, the pond, and the clover-covered fields. "Wow, I could totally live here!"

"Um, you practically do," I remind her. Her ranch is out in the middle of nowhere.

"Oh, yeah," she says. "I don't go outside enough. I need to put a big picnic table like this in the back, and we could live out there."

"You're outside a lot in the summer, though. Are you singing at any festivals this year?"

"The normal bluegrass one in Kansas." Vanessa is popular in her area for her bluegrass songs and hymns. "A wedding in August, and the Strawberry Festival in Stillwell. That's it."

"I can't believe you're not famous yet!" I say, like I do every time I see her. "Are you sure you're too old for American Idol?"

"Yep. You have to be under twenty-eight. But, I don't have time to be famous anyway. I have kids to raise."

"True." I laugh. "I don't have time to be famous either. Otherwise, I'd be all over it."

Vanessa's daughter runs up to get another juice box and some grapes.

"How's school going?" I ask her. I'm always curious about kids in regular school. "What do you learn in third grade?"

"Oh, we mostly get ready for the Oklahoma test we take." She unwraps her straw and pokes it in the juice box.

"But I mean, what kinds of stuff do you do when you're not practicing for the test?" I ask her again. "Like art or music or history or geography? What's your favorite thing to learn about?"

"We mostly just practice for the test," she shrugs. "We don't have music and art anymore. We used to, last year, but this year we don't." She runs off to play Duck, Duck, Goose.

Vanessa looks at me. "Great, right? I'm sure they do other stuff, but they really do practice for this test a lot. They came home and told me the other day, 'We have to do well on the test or the teachers don't get any money!' No pressure for the kids, right?" She smiles wryly.

"Oh, wow. That's crazy."

"Yes, and my sister teaches at a high school in Texas," Vanessa continues. "She told me that out of one hundred and eighty days of instruction, forty five are spent on getting ready for or taking the test."

"What? That's almost a fourth of the year!"

"Yep. The kids have practice tests, and more practice tests to prepare for those practice tests. They don't read great literature; they read sentences on their practice test. They don't learn about great men and women of history; they memorize some dates and a few vocabulary words." Vanessa pauses a minute. "And, next year they are supposed to have a sex-ed class."

"No way! In fourth grade?"

"Yeah, they'll be *nine*. It's ridiculous. There's no telling what the class will teach. I asked the school to tell me when it's scheduled so I can keep them home that week, but who knows if they'll remember. In fact…you won't believe this, but because of all our reservations we were considering pulling the kids out and homeschooling."

"What? You said you'd *never* homeschool!"

"I know! Can you believe it? But, Eric isn't sold on it yet. He just doesn't know many people that homeschool, and it still seems a little weird to him. Plus, he wants the kids to have an influence for Christ in their schools. He became a Christian that way—a school friend invited him to church—so he feels like there's a need for Christians in the schools." Vanessa pauses and chews on her lip. "I don't know though, it seems like my kids are becoming more like their friends than the other way around. Well, Kyle does okay; he's pretty strong. But Courtney is more of a follower and tends to do what everyone else is doing. She comes home rolling her eyes and talking back to me. I'm a little worried about her, actually."

Vanessa sighs and brushes a strand of blonde hair out of her eyes. "It's so hard, isn't it? It's such a big decision."

"It is so hard." I nod. "Have you prayed about it?"

"Well, yes. And for now, I feel like the answer is: I need to respect Eric's wishes and keep the kids in public school. But, I don't know—I am having more and more of a heart to keep them home. We'll just have to see. So for the next year, we're going to supplement a bit of the academics at home—read more in the evenings, do some art and music, that kind of thing. And I'll keep praying about the whole thing."

"Wow, so they'll be going to school, *and* you'll be teaching them at night!" I laugh. "They'll be getting twice the education!"

"True, I never thought if it that way! I should tell that to all those women at church who think I'm a bad mother for not homeschooling!"

"What? You, a bad mother? Are they insane?"

"Oh, you know—they just think all good Christian mothers should homeschool. Surely I must be crazy if I'm not."

"Well, I have plenty of people who think I am crazy because I am homeschooling!" I am thinking of Vicky and John's grandmother. "So, at least it evens out. Ooh, maybe we can just trade places and everyone will be happy."

"There's no way to make everyone happy." Vanessa shrugs. "Someone is always going to criticize us for something. But, we're not serving them, are we? We're serving the Lord."

"That's what my Mom always says! She always quotes Galatians 1:10, 'For if I still pleased men, I would not be a bondservant of Christ.'"

"Exactly!" Vanessa's blue eyes light up. "I love that verse. But I always think of it as 'if I still pleased women' or 'if I still pleased other mothers' because sometimes I realize that's what I'm trying to do: please all the other mothers in the world so they'll think I'm a good mom. But, I have to just do what will please the Lord."

"Totally," I agree. "That's one of the biggest things God has taught me this year. I can't please everyone, and I can't focus on what they think. God calls mothers to all different places, schools, choices. We are all doing what we think is best for our children. God seems to have called our family to homeschool for this season. So, I just need to obey and leave the results up to Him."

Vanessa nods, then ponders for a moment, looking off at the distant fields. "Hey, it's like the sheep!"

"Huh?"

"You know, the sheep. How Dr. D. was telling us about how the mother sheep listen to the Shepherd's voice? So, these mommy sheep are caring for their little lambs, and they might take them to this pasture, or that pond for a drink or whatever, but they are *all listening to the voice of the Shepherd to tell them where to go.*"

"Yeah!" I finally get what she's talking about. "And they don't all sit around and criticize the other mommy sheep because they're not exactly like them! They're each mothering their little lambs in the way they think best, and they are following their Good Shepherd."

"Trust and Obey." Vanessa nods. This is another thing I love about her. Since she sings bluegrass and hymns all the time, she always has those words in her heart and mind. It's like she speaks Hymn. It's awesome.

"In fact," I tell her, "my friend Elizabeth just had twins. She has been homeschooling for years, but she's feeling a bit overwhelmed. She's not sure what she's going to do next year."

"I can certainly understand that!" Vanessa's twins were unbelievably fussy babies, I remember. They alternated sleep schedules, so she and her husband never got more than an hour or two of sleep at a time for about six months. They were starting to hallucinate from sleep deprivation. It was brutal.

"I talked to Elizabeth the other day," I say, "and she said they were thinking about putting her kindergarten-aged son in the public school down the street in the fall. But, on the other hand, she feels like even if she can't do a lot of 'school' with him each day, he is learning about caring for others, helping their family, sacrifice, all good character lessons. So, they're still deciding. She knows if it's what the Lord leads them to do, He'll help her find a way to do it. There's no way her twins can be as hard as yours were, though!" I smile at Vanessa. We both know it's true.

"It was so *ridiculously* hard," Vanessa agrees. "In fact, I remember when the twins were born, someone had given me a gift basket with some delicious-smelling soap. When the babies were crying, I'd leave them in their cribs for a few minutes and go into the bathroom and sit there smelling soap! It was the one moment of peace in my day. How sad is that?"

"That's so pitiful," I laugh. "That's the best the day got, smelling a bar of soap! Wow, see our lives are so much easier than they were with newborns, I have to remember that!"

We look over at Michael. He is running in circles; that's what he does when he's excited. His tummy goes first, as though the rest of him can't quite keep up, and his bottom waggles from side to side. He hitches his arms up at the elbows, swinging them wildly and running on his pudgy baby legs with short, choppy steps. He's like a tiny, crazy, tin soldier.

A tiny, crazy, tin soldier in pink socks. I forgot his shoes, again. I am forever forgetting my children's shoes. What is wrong with me? Normal mothers remember shoes. I had to dig in the car for whatever I could find, and what I found was a pair of Joy's pink socks. That's one advantage of having weeks worth of junk in the car. I'll point that out to John the next time he marvels at the depth of the mess: "See, if the car was all clean and spotless like yours, I wouldn't have had those handy pink socks!"

I've always been awful with shoes. I remember when Daniel was a couple months old or so, and I had to drag myself out of my pink, fleece, polar-bear pajama bottoms into actual clothes and make it to our first library story time. Daniel was still in his yellow, footed, teddy-bear jammies; I hadn't had time to get him dressed or change his diaper if we wanted to make it to story time. It started at ten o'clock! Practically the crack of dawn!

So, we went in and as the librarian read, I looked around. The other mothers all had on cute jeans and looked like they had not only showered but *fixed their hair.* The babies happened to all be girls, and I noticed that not one of them was in her pajamas, and some of them had those stretchy ribbons around their heads and shoes with bows on them. Not just shoes. *Shoes with bows on them.*

I was floored. I don't think I had even considered that babies wear shoes. I was like, "Oh, shoes! Right! We should get some of those!" But I was wondering, because that seemed kind of basic—what else had I forgotten?

It's like last summer when I observed Joy's ballet class. There was one pudgy two-year-old in class because her big sister was in the class too. All the other girls would be doing their *demi-plies* and *piques* on the barre and as soon as she'd turn the right way, they'd be on to the next step. She tried so hard, bless her heart, but she could never get caught up. That's how I felt— like everyone knew the right steps except me, and I was bluffing my way through. Like I was perpetually one step behind.

I'm realizing, though, seven years into this mothering thing, that lots of moms feel that way. I was talking to a friend of mine about how I wanted to use real plates instead of paper "when I get it together" and she rolled her eyes and said, "Oh, right, like you don't have it together." Seriously? Have you not *seen* my car? But I realized she *hadn't* seen my car, and she'd never heard me snapping angrily at my kids. She hadn't seen me on those mornings when we should have been starting school, but Daniel and Joy were still in the living room watching *Peter Pan,* and Michael was in the kitchen eating brown sugar out of the canister, while I (their attentive and conscientious mother) sat in the office at the computer, laughing at the Pioneer Woman blog. My friend thought I, of all people, was a perfect mom. I tried to explain that I struggle all the time, with so many things, but I don't think she believed me. We are so hard on ourselves, we mothers.

But God, our benevolent Teacher, is watching us mothers with a smile, isn't He? He's not mad at us for the missteps; He's encouraging us to dance. He knows we're doing the best we can; He's proud of us for trying; His love for our sweet and clumsy selves fills the room.

"How's Michael doing on his weight?" Vanessa asks. I had told her about the whole not-gaining-weight thing.

"Much, much better." I watch him fall down laughing. "He's actually back up to the first percentile now—he's back on the charts! Woo-hoo! It's probably about time to wean him totally, but I can't bring myself to stop. We both love that nursing time so much and it's such a sweet time of baby-ness. He's probably going to be our last one."

"You always say that!" Vanessa laughs at me.

"I do?"

"Yes! You said that with Daniel and Joy, too, I remember."

"Oh, well this time I really mean it!" I do. Really.

"Mommy, look what I found in the grass!" Joy runs over to show me something in her hand. "It's a robin's egg!" She shows me the fragile, turquoise egg, still mostly intact but with a crack and hole in one side.

"Ooh, what a treasure!" I breathe. "Where did you find it?"

"It was under that tree over there!" Joy gestures to a big elm. "I guess the bird cracked out and flew away. See?" She shows Vanessa. "See, there was a little baby birdie in there. A robin. The mommy robin sits on it and sits on it and sits on it for years! Well, maybe not years, maybe a few months? Or weeks? Anyway, then one day, it cracks out of the egg. I don't know how it cracks out?...but it does ...then it sits in the nest and the mommy bird brings it worms and it says 'chirp, chirp, chirp' because its brother and sister birds are there and they all want food and they say 'me , me, Mommy, feed me!' and the mommy feeds it the worms and then it says 'thank you, Mommy,' well, not really, it just eats the worms, and then it gets bigger and bigger and then it flies out of the nest! And that's the end! Then it's a big robin!" Joy stops to take a breath. "I wonder if I can find the nest?" She sets the egg gently on the picnic table, asks me to watch it, then runs off again.

"Whew!" I laugh. "She's my talker, all right!"

"That's amazing though!" Vanessa raises her eyebrows at me. "How does she know that? Have you guys been studying birds?"

"Well, not really studied in a book or anything, but we have a robin's nest right by our back door so John lifts up the kids to see the baby birds. It's funny, I can plan and plan, but a lot of learning sort of comes to us. Usually in quiet moments, or outside."

Michael runs over for more juice. He points into the field with horses.

"Caw!" he says.

"Horse!" I tell him.

"C-ow!" he enunciates clearly this time.

"No, Michael, that's a horse!" I smile into his big brown eyes.

He looks at me with eyebrows raised and very, very clearly and loudly, corrects me: "COW!" Vanessa and I crack up.

We look over to the field where the kids are running through the clover.

"Hey, we should make clover crowns!" Vanessa says. "The clover is long. It's perfect."

"Teach me how." I follow Vanessa and we sit down on the grass.

"Around and around and through." She shows me. "I learned this from an old book; isn't it great? Why don't kids make flower crowns anymore?"

We sit in the field, as the kids run and tumble and laugh, while we twist clover crowns for them.

*Around and around and through. Around and around and through.* This, I can give my children, I realize. This, they need. In an age of electronic toys and standardized tests, of hurry and stress, we all need this. Time to sit and be quiet, surrounded by horses and sheep, clouds and clover, to work tranquilly in a field, plucking bits of April sweetness.

Vanessa and I weave silently, together, in the golden afternoon. The clover crowns will break by this evening and life will move on. Babies will grow up; children will grow tall. But right now, we have childhood and lengthening shadows and quiet minutes and clover crowns.

*****

The kids are in the back of the car and we are all headed home to Tulsa, exhausted and peaceful, after our day at the sheep farm. Joy and Michael are asleep.

I'm thinking about what Vanessa said, about us caring for our little flocks. The trip to the sheep farm is like a parenting lesson for me, better than any class. My job is as a mother, to guide my little sheep gently. I still feel like I don't know what I'm doing, but I'm willing to follow the Good Shepherd, who gently leads those who have young.

I always feel better after these trips to the country, out in Creation, away from all the things I think are so important.

As I drive, I think of the dancing light on the children's hair, the crowns of flowers, the honesty and simplicity. Suddenly, it hits me.

I know what to get Frank and Vicky for their anniversary.

Bible
- Completed Awana Sparks Book, attended Club weekly
- Memorized 33 Bible verses in Sparks book
- Read Bible with family (various Children's Bibles throughout year) and Sunday School
- Hymns – memorized 8 hymns, at least one verse and chorus

Math:
- Finished math workbook
- Hands-on math (fractions, telling time, measuring, weighing)
- Spatial Skills – puzzles, LEGOs, tangrams, geoboards, unifix cubes
- Charts, Graphs, Maps – read maps, charted temperatures and Lego box heights, made graphs

Language Arts: Vocabulary, Reading Skills – Reading Alone
- Read 10 minutes many days, 16 Easy Reader books (see book list)
- Reads to Michael occasionally, maybe 2x/week

Language Arts: Vocabulary, Comprehension – Reading Together
- Read 107 picture books (see book list), plus lots I forgot to write down
- Listened to 28 books on CD (see book list)
- Read 7 chapter books at night with family (see book list)

# ~ May ~

We are on our way to Dallas for Frank and Vicky's 40th Anniversary Party. It's a four-hour drive without kids and a six-hour drive with kids. We left at 2 p.m. from Tulsa hoping Michael would nap and he did! He's waking up now, cranky and sweaty, so we're about to stop at a McDonald's with a play area to eat an early dinner and let everyone run around for a while.

I am so sick of McDonald's. John's busy season at work was mid-January through mid-April and he had to work a lot of evenings and every Saturday. John and I decided we needed a Date Night so every Sunday night we went to McDonald's or Burger King so the kids could play at the play area while we actually got to talk. I want John to know that even though I spend so much time and energy on homeschooling, I still want to make time for him. Because, what could be more romantic than French fries and a play area with screaming children? Oh well; it works. My husband and I get to talk, the kids get to run around, and we all get to eat something, though perhaps not the most nourishing food on the planet. Today we eat, then the kids want to go play.

"May I be excused, please?" Daniel asks, after he inhales his chicken nuggets.

"Well, we need to do your spelling test. Then you can play," I tell Daniel. I know it's a Friday afternoon, but we need to finish up our last spelling test of the year. I brought his spelling book and notebook in with me. John takes Joy and Michael away from the table.

"Mom, do I *have* to?" Daniel whines. "I don't have to write the words *down*, do I? Can I just say them?"

"No, I want you to write them down. You need to practice writing."

"How about I write half of them down?" Daniel begins to bargain with me.

"Daniel, listen to me." I look into his eyes and speak slowly and clearly. "You are going to write *all* the words down. Please don't complain or argue about it anymore. I've told you the answer. If you can't have a cheerful attitude, that tells me you need more practice, okay?"

"Okay," Daniel mumbles with a deep sigh of despair and misery.

"Try again," I say cheerfully. "Give me a big smile and say 'Okay, Mom!'"

Daniel grits his teeth and bares them in what could be called a smile. If you were a rabid dog. Or a grizzly bear. "Okay, Mom." That will work.

"Great!" I say in a chipper, excited-about-spelling voice. "Here's your notebook and pencil. Your first word is 'patch.'"

Daniel stares out the window a bit, writes the word, then sighs, as if exhausted by the effort.

"Great! Now, remember, when you're done, say 'I'm done, Mom.'"

"I'm done, Mom," Daniel mumbles.

"Great! Your next word is 'such.'" I take a sip of my Diet Coke. John is playing Eggs Crackin' Out with Joy. Michael is blissfully throwing Joy's Happy Meal toy into the slide and catching it. It's one of those Zoobles, those balls that turn into an animal when you drop them. It's pretty much Michael's dream toy. I look back at Daniel. He's playing with his pencil, pretending it's a rocket-ship.

"Daniel, are you done?"

"Oh! Yes, sorry!" Daniel looks at me guiltily, knowing he forgot. "I'm done, Mom!"

"Okay, good job, buddy. Your next word is 'Mr.'" I have gotten more patient with this part of school. I listened to a great CD from the homeschool convention about teaching "highly distractible children." It was awesome. The speaker gave lots of ideas of games to do, but she also said that she realized part of her job is to help her son stay focused on his work. He needed help, just like Daniel, and that's part of our job as teachers. It's still a little irritating after the three-hundredth time I remind Daniel, but my ceiling for annoyance is higher than it used to be.

I suspect that if Daniel had been in school last year he would have been diagnosed with ADD and prescribed Ritalin, he had so much trouble concentrating. I'm pretty sure he's just a normal seven-year-old boy though. Here, homeschooling is a tremendous advantage. I know him better than anyone and can give him what he needs. With lots of breaks, movement-based learning games, some help staying focused, and attention to his diet (protein for breakfast and no sugar), he's doing great. His attention has improved leaps and bounds since only one year ago. And, he's whining and crying much less during school, though we still have some issues.

Daniel writes the word and a few more. Then he whines, "Mom, how many more *are there?*"

"Don't worry about it. Focus on the one we're on," I tell him gently. "But Daniel, that was a complaining voice, so that tells me you need a little more practice doing this cheerfully, so I'm going to give you one extra one for practice at the end. Now, let's try to do the rest cheerfully without complaining, okay?"

"All right," Daniel says, suddenly stoic. "That's okay, I wanted to do an extra one anyway!" He thinks that somehow by pretending to enjoy the punishment it will make it better.

Which is fine by me. Go ahead, enjoy the fire out of yourself as you write that extra spelling word.

We do a few more words, then Joy runs over. "I want to do school too!" she begs. Today for her spring ensemble Joy has selected: her purple planet shirt from the Tulsa Planetarium, khaki cutoff shorts, red Santa Claus knee socks, black patent-leather Mary Janes, and a string of fake pearls. (Daniel is wearing three Star Wars LEGO shirts, layered on top of each other, so that "if one gets dirty, I can just take it off and still have two left!")

"Okay, here Joy, read this word to Daniel," I point to a word in the spelling book.

Joy is sounding out the word to herself, "Mmm-aaaa-tttt-kkkk....matk?"

" Well, 'c-h' together says, 'chuh' remember?" I prompt her. "So, mm-aaa-chuh...say it fast...and it's...? "

"Match!" Joy figures out.

"Great! You did it!" I give her a squeeze. She skips off again to play with Michael. "Daniel write that word down, please."

"What?" Daniel was staring out the window again, watching the birds hopping around on the grass.

"Match. Write down 'match,' please," I instruct him.

"Okay." Daniel writes it down. "Is that right?"

"Well, look at it," I answer patiently. "Does it look right to you?"

"I don't know!" Daniel is frustrated by that question, but I don't want to give him the answer. "Yes?"

"Just do your best guess and at the end I'll help you correct it if you need to."

"Okay." Daniel decides it's correct and we move on. We finish all twelve words, plus two extras, one for complaining and one for being silly (I have started giving extra words for that too, since he could waste hours of my time by being silly while I'm trying to help him). He missed one word, so I show him and he rewrites it. Finally we're done.

"Can I go play now?" Daniel asks, looking exhausted.

"Yes! Go play! Excellent work, Daniel. You are such a good speller!" I give him a big hug. "Remember the beginning of the year? You had trouble writing even a few words! Look how well you're doing now!"

"Yeah, great job, buddy!" John comes over and gives him a big hug and kiss on the head. "You worked so diligently this year! Look, you finished that whole spelling book!"

"It was easy," Daniel shrugs, embarrassed now. That was easy? What would hard look like? Daniel goes off to play in the play area.

"Dah-nuh! Wash!" Michael is shouting over by the slide.

"I'm coming to watch, Michael! I'm coming," Daniel grins and goes to play ball with Michael.

John comes to sit with me at the table.

"Whew!" I say, taking a handful of fries. "We're done. I'm exhausted."

"No kidding," John says, with raised eyebrows. "That looked painful."

"Yeah, that's pretty much writing every day. Math is better though. It's actually all a lot better than the beginning of the year."

"Wow. Good job, honey," John says, admiringly.

"Thanks. Okay, I can write that down for Turmoil. I was having trouble thinking of something." I have this Treasures & Turmoil Journal that stays in the car. I started writing in it with Elizabeth when we would go to a play area with our kids—we'd write down what our Treasures were about each of our children at that moment, and what was our Turmoil. It was really fun to go back and read what special things each child was doing on a particular day, and also to see what the hard things were. We saw how quickly the hard things passed. By the time we went back and read the journal, we'd forgotten all about them.

I write "spelling tests" down in the Turmoil section of the journal, then John and I add more Treasures for each child. The kids are still contentedly playing so we can talk some more.

"So, what goals do you have for this year?" John asks me. My birthday was last week, but we haven't gone out to celebrate yet because we were getting ready for this trip. John knows that I am a nerd and like to think about goals for each year. And because I am so exceedingly nerdy, I turn to a new page in the Treasures & Turmoil notebook and write at the top of the page: Goals for 35.

Suddenly, it hits me: "I'm thirty-five!" I tell John in shock.

"Um, yes?" he says, a bit surprised that I am just now realizing this.

"*Thirty-five*! I'm old!" I exclaim.

"You're not *old*." John rolls his eyes. He is forty-two, so he gets mildly annoyed when I talk about how old I am.

"No, I *am*! It's different for women. Thirty-five is the marker. It was always ahead of me, like a sign way up the road, at the top of the hill. Now, I'm passing the sign! I'm on my way down the hill! I'm...*over the hill!* Now, I see why they say that! I'm considered high-risk, if we have any more kids."

John chokes a bit on his water. "Do you *want* more kids?" We had settled on three. Kind of.

"No. I don't. I *don't* want more kids..." I try to explain, "but I don't *not* want more kids."

"What?" he laughs.

"I can't imagine life without a baby! How can we live without a baby in our house? It just seems so...empty." I haven't really thought all of this through, so I'm processing as I talk, but John's used to that.

"I mean, I don't want to be pregnant. I really don't. I'm not excited about gaining forty pounds again. And I very much enjoy sleeping through the night. But, what if we wouldn't have had Michael? I can't imagine!"

"I know, that's true." John nods his head. "He's not even two yet, though. Maybe we could wait a year or two? And, there's always adoption."

"Right," I say. We've talked about adoption before. I almost can't imagine not bringing a child who needs a loving family into our home. But maybe not tomorrow.

"I think you have until forty until you have to worry about being too old," John reasons with me. "Lots of people have babies after thirty-five. How old is Elizabeth?"

"I think she's forty," I say. We do know lots of people who had babies up to, and over, forty. So I guess I don't have to freak out today.

"We still have a while to decide," John says, calmly. How is he always so rational? I don't get it. "We can think about it."

What is wrong with me? Life is just now getting more manageable—I can actually dream that we'll get something done in school next year. I've finally gotten back into my size eight jeans (my stomach didn't seem to have gotten the same message the rest of my body did, but whatever).

But I tried to give away the baby clothes in the attic a few weeks ago and couldn't do it. I can't imagine no more pudgy baby legs in shorts, no more flowered onesie sundresses and tiny sandals. I can't imagine life without the giggles and laughter and antics of a little one.

It's all the Duggars' fault. I see how life with nineteen kids is exhausting and busy, crazy and loud. I know it's a reality TV show and all but, boy, those children have a rich life. What love surrounds them daily, what friendship. I see how much richer Daniel's and Joy's lives are because of their baby brother. I know God gives some wonderful families no children, or only one or two, but for me to *choose* to have just three children in a family? It seems so…incomplete. I'm not saying I want nineteen? But maybe more than three.

"All right, we can think about it later," I agree. "Anyway, how are you? How was work this week?"

"Good. I finished up the Second National Bank proposal, and went to that training class on Wednesday. I got a few reports filed that were overdue." John pauses, which means he has something else to say. I have to just sit and wait for him to decide to tell me what it is. It's like he has to think of the exact way to say it, or make sure I'm really paying attention or something.

"And, I found out I'm getting a bonus," he finally says nonchalantly.

"What?" I yelp. "Hello? You got a *bonus*?"

"Yeah," he says, eyes twinkling now, knowing he's in trouble for not telling me right away.

"John!" I say, playfully chastising him. "These are the things to tell your wife! Remember, you're supposed to tell me the *most important* things first! Not like, 'Oh, I put on my shoes. Then I ate breakfast. And *then I got a bonus!*'"

"I know, I know!" he says, laughing. "Sorry, I forgot to tell you! We've been busy!"

I heave a big sigh. "How much is it, do you know?"

"Um, three thousand?" John says, looking embarrassed.

"*Three thousand dollars*? John! Argh!!! You're killing me!" I fling myself down on the table in mock agony.

"What's wrong, Mommy?" Joy asks, not sure if there's really something wrong or not.

"Oh, nothing, sweetie. Your Daddy is just funny, that's all." I smile at her, trying to be a bit less dramatic so she doesn't think something's really wrong.

"Oh." Joy looks at us like we're both weird and goes back to playing.

I think I am going to come up with a questionnaire for John to fill out when he gets home.

    1)  Did you get a raise, promotion, or bonus today?
        Yes/No  Amount: _____

2) Did you get fired today?  Yes/No
3) Are you travelling out of the state/country anytime soon?  Yes/No  Date: _____
4) What else happened today that you think your wife wouldn't care about: _____

It's a good thing men can't get pregnant, otherwise John would be six months along before he would remember to tell me about it. Sheesh.

"Great job, honey! I'm so proud of you!" I grin at John. "You've been putting in all those extra hours, finding clients, getting stuff out on time. Oh, and, you're brilliant." Vanessa's brother-in-law not only hired John's firm to audit their small bank, but referred them to every other bank in the area that was hit with the new requirements. John and his staff will be driving a bit more, but that's okay. They are thrilled to have the work.

John laughs, looking happy and relieved. I guess if they gave him a bonus he can relax that they're not going to fire him anytime soon.

"We should celebrate!" I smile at him.

"What would we do?" John asks.

"I don't know—you could splurge! You could get, you know, a *Coke,* instead of water!" I suggest.

"Yeah, I could," John says, uncertainly.

"Actually, the drinks are only a dollar here," I remind him. "It's a bargain! You should totally get a Coke, honey." This whole conversation is utterly ridiculous, but John hates spending money for drinks at restaurants. We'll be at Olive Garden or something, and I'll try to convince him to get a Coke and he'll shake his head and say, "It's $2.25! You could get a whole 2-liter for that!" He just can't do it. It's the accountant in him. I, on the other hand, have no problem whatsoever with this.

"I'll go get you one," I decide. "And an ice cream sundae. To celebrate. Okay?"

"Okay," John smiles. "That sounds great."

*****

We leave McDonald's, then stop for gas before getting back on the highway. John is going to run inside to the ATM while I wait in the car with the kids.

"Daddy, please can I go in with you? I'm *burning!*" Joy begs from her sunny car seat. The car was hot when we left the restaurant and hasn't cooled off sufficiently in the thirty seconds we've been in the car, apparently.

"No, I'm just going to run in real quick." John gets out of the car and starts to shut the door.

"Daddy, please, *please!* I'm so hot!" Joy pleads.

"Daddy, can I go, *please*? I'll get back in my seat super-quick!" Daniel begs. Really? The gas station is so much more interesting than waiting in the car? Do they think they're going to die of boredom or be incinerated in the two minutes it takes for the car to cool off?

"You'll be fine. The air conditioner is on." John shuts the car door and goes into the gas station.

Daniel and Joy are still moaning about who's the hottest. "Good thing you're not as hot as me, Joy!" Daniel says. "I have pools of sweat under my seat."

"Daniel, I don't think you have *pools* of sweat under your seat," I say, trying not to laugh. "Drops, maybe."

"Oh, I think there are pools," he says, sounding completely convinced he's about to perish from dehydration.

"I'm burning!" Joy is moaning. The air conditioner is on full-blast and by now it's not even warm in the car; they have just worked themselves up.

I get out of the car to check on the gas progress and also to avoid the moaning. I have to laugh a bit to myself though. When they're exaggerating, I always have to remember that quote from *Father of the Bride*, "Why would I *overreact*? No one in my *family* overreacts." Ahem.

I finish pumping the gas and John comes back out to the car.

"We are removing the stick from this vehicle." I hear him tell the kids. I look in and notice Joy waving a huge stick around. Oops. "Why is there a big stick in the car?" he asks me.

"I don't know—they collect them? Who knows?" I answer. The kids do collect a lot of sticks, Very Special and Important Sticks, which join their collection of Very Special and Important Rocks on the floorboards of the car. You never know what you'll find in our car. The side panels, I mean Secret Hideouts, are full of LEGOs, Happy Meal toys, and Joy's bracelets and rubber bands. But, if we're ever stuck in a snowstorm, maybe we could fashion a campfire out of the sticks and rocks, light it with the cigarette lighter, and survive until we are rescued. I'm just saying: there might be an upside we haven't considered.

I climb into the passenger seat; John gets in the driver's seat. He drives across the parking lot to the grass beside the building. "Sorry guys, you were about to whack Michael in the head with the stick. It's not safe." John throws the stick into the grass, amidst cries of protest.

"Who wants to watch Dora?" I ask, hoping to distract Daniel and Joy.

"Me! Me!" they both shout. I know I speak disparagingly of technology sometimes, but that doesn't include car trips. Or airplane trips. Or when I'm really tired. On those days, the DVD player is my best friend. (I wonder what Farmer Boy's parents did on long wagon trips?)

We turn on Dora and start driving. Surprisingly Michael likes this and doesn't scream for a while. We also brought the Duke vs. Butler game in case he gets antsy. Michael won't watch

Praise Baby or Baby Einstein or any normal baby movies, but he begs often to "wash bah-keh-bah?" During the NCAA tournament my Dad made a DVD of the championship game and sent it to us. Michael thinks it's the best thing ever. It feeds his basketball obsession.

The other thing Michael is obsessed with is Daddy, which is fine with me, honestly. It's nice. When John gets home Michael runs to the door and screams, "Dah-Dah! Bah-ket-bah! Shoot! Ow-sigh!" Which, roughly translated, means "Daddy, come play basketball outside with me, right now, or I'll ask you all night until you give in." Playing basketball means Michael standing on a chair and putting the ball in his Little Tykes basket and Daddy cheering.

"I thought we banned Dora for car drives," John is saying now as we pull onto the interstate.

"I forgot," I groan.

Dora's exceedingly loud and annoying voice is shrieking, "I CAN'T HEAR YOU!" and our kids are screaming in reply, "THE MAP! THE MAP!" A few minutes later, Dora has convinced them to bellow, "AYÚDAME! AYÚDAME!" which I happen to know means, "HELP ME! HELP ME!"

Dora, my enthusiastic little friend, I think the parents are the ones that need help here.

*****

Ginger invited my parents and Holly's family to the party too. We're all staying at the same hotel. It's Sunday afternoon and I'm starting to get nervous. What if Frank and Vicky hate the surprise gift I have planned for them? I take a deep breath and try not to think about it. It's too late now, anyway.

Holly and I dress the children and send them down to the lobby with John and Jay with explicit instructions for the dads to try and get as many wiggles out of the kids as possible. Holly and I are dressing in my room while my parents get ready in their room.

"Wow, Julianne!" Holly stares at me when I come out of the bathroom. "You look fantastic! You've lost a ton of weight!"

"Really, it's only about ten pounds since Christmas." This has been the slowest baby weight loss ever, but I'm glad I'm finally done. I feel like myself again.

Sabrina went shopping with me and helped me pick out an incredible sapphire beaded gown. She made me buy heels and promise to wear makeup. I did.

"It's not just looking skinny though, or the dress," Holly says. "You're glowing! You look amazing!"

"Thanks, Holly! You look amazing too!" Holly is wearing a slate taffeta dress with a gorgeous jeweled neckline. It's very Oscar-red-carpet.

"I think we both look stunning!" I give Holly a hug. "We must be related or something. Now, let's see how long we can go before someone poops, throws up, or wipes their noses on us!" We go down to the lobby to meet our husbands and children.

"Whoa, honey!" John gapes at me when we walk off the elevator. "Wow." That's all he can say.

"Wow, yourself." I wink at him. He looks stunning in his tuxedo, as he smiles at me with his blue-green eyes twinkling. I am a lucky woman.

Daniel and Michael are wearing the miniature tuxedos my mom insisted on buying them for the party. Emma toddles around, holding Joy's hand. They look like tiny and tinier fairies in pink gossamer dresses, like models for a wedding catalog.

Only in this catalog, the models are petite Hoth Rebel Troopers. "You can be the Clone Gunner," Daniel says to Joy. "So, you'll be fighting Battle Droids in the desert." Joy is helping Emma adjust the bow in her hair and ignores him. He considers

Joy's uninterested silence to be unspoken consent, and goes on, "Emma can be a Battle Droid, I'll be Luke Skywalker, and Michael can be..." he trails off, thinking for a minute.

"An Ewok?" I offer. Ewoks are about the only thing I remember from Star Wars. It's all a mystery to me. Daniel looks at me doubtfully, "Well, if he was an Ewok, then he'd have to be on Endor with Han...but, I guess that's okay. Dad could be a storm trooper, and Uncle Jay can be Mace Windu." It's like a foreign language to me. He might as well be speaking Swahili.

"Well, we can all play that, but it's going to have to be tomorrow, because we have to go, buddy."

"Awww, man!" Daniel pouts. I feel bad for squashing his ideas so often, but he just has so *many* of them, so many plans for the world. It's exhausting.

My dad takes some family pictures, then we all head over to Dave and Ginger's house. We get stuck in traffic, so we're running a little late. We pull up to the house, a stone castle, more or less, with valets to park the cars for tonight's special occasion. We walk around to the backyard as the sun sinks behind the trees.

The backyard looks incredible. Round tables draped with white linen tablecloths dot the lawn. Each table has an enormous bouquet of yellow roses, purple lavender, and fragrant stargazer lilies; smaller flowers are twisted into garlands around the patio columns.

"Mom, look!" Daniel gasps, pointing. "Lily pads!" I look and on the pool are floating real lily pads, a tiny flickering candle nestled inside each creamy blossom.

"Ooh, those are beautiful!" I say, and grab his hand, as well as Joy's. I remind John not to let Michael out of his sight. Michael is fast; he could be over to that pool before we even realized he was gone.

"Look, Daddy! Diamonds!" Joy exclaims, pointing up. We look up, and I gasp. There is an immense chandelier hanging from a stately oak tree in the center of the yard, turning the backyard into an elegant ballroom. The cut-glass teardrops glimmer like jewels in the candlelight. How did Ginger pull *that* off?

"Hi, guys!" Ginger comes up to greet us, wearing a shimmering gown with a neckline that showcases her ruby and diamond drop-pendant.

"Ginger, I knew this would be amazing but, wow! I am impressed. Are Frank and Vicky here?"

"Yes, they're over there talking to some friends. They were completely surprised! I can't believe they didn't find out! Take a few minutes to mingle before dinner, okay?"

John introduces me to Luisa and Maria, the families' housekeepers, who both have the night off; they and their families are attending as guests. Maria hugs us all and pronounces Joy a "chica bonita." Daniel and Joy practice their Spanish with Maria's grandchildren.

We greet John's grandmother, who is so awed with the beautiful party that she forgets to tell us how horrendous it is that we're homeschooling. We manage to avoid the topic completely, then slip off to talk to some other guests.

A woman on the catering staff plays a few melodic notes on a xylophone to let us know it's time to sit down for dinner. We sit next to a lovely elderly Aunt Anne who John barely knew growing up. She's about ninety and she's wearing a butter-colored suit, probably Chanel. Oh dear. She looks very refined. *Please behave*, I silently will the kids.

But what's this? She's whispering in Joy's ear and her eyes are sparkling with mischief. Now she and Joy start doing a hand clap rhyme: "Miss Mary Mack, Mack, Mack, all dressed in black, black, black ..." Well this is unexpected. Now she's teaching Daniel. Maybe we'll be okay after all.

We finish our herb bread and salads, and the servers come to brush the crumbs off our table with a tiny silver tool (that Aunt Anne tells us is called a crumber, logically) before the main course. That seems a bit over the top for a party in the backyard, but these are John's parents we're talking about. A sudden wave of fear washes over me. What if Frank and Vicky hate my surprise? It's not exactly their style. What if they never speak to me again?

I have an image of myself sitting alone at Christmas, huddled up crying into my eggnog, while John and the kids go to Christmas at his parent's house without me. I'll be an outcast and —

"You okay, Jules?" John asks, looking at me with concern.

"Me? Oh yeah, great." I take a gulp of water.

"It's going to be wonderful. They're going to love it." John squeezes my hand.

"Maybe. Or they might never speak to me again."

"Unlikely," John says, winking at me.

The servers bring out the next course — bacon-wrapped filet mignon, grilled shrimp in butter sauce, and asparagus with shaved parmesan curls. Maybe this will help quiet all those butterflies in my stomach.

Michael got a turn at "clap-clap," and now Aunt Anne is telling them knock-knock jokes while they eat. Okay, Aunt Anne totally rocks. We should bring her with us every time we go out to eat.

"You sure have wonderful children," Aunt Anne says to me.

"Praise the Lord," I say, gratefully. "And thank you for entertaining them!"

I look over to Ginger's table. She smiles reassuringly. She knows what's going on. It's almost time.

The servers whisk away our plates and bring out the dessert. We have the choice between crème *brûlée* and molten chocolate cake. I choose crème *brûlée*, but I can only eat a bite. My stomach is in knots.

As we finish dessert, Dave gets up and goes to the microphone on the back patio. He and John decided that he should go first since he's the older brother. He tells some funny stories about growing up, then gives a toast to his mom and dad. Now it's John's turn. He gets up and starts to speak into the microphone.

"Thank you all for coming tonight. It means so much to my father and mother. We have a little surprise for you."

My heart is pounding. I'm watching Frank's and Vicky's reactions. Ginger smiles at me reassuringly from her table. She knows what's going on.

"My father met my mother when he was in medical school. That year was 1969. They met at a social event, a country and western dance. He saw my mother across the room and asked her to dance. The song they danced to, my mother told us when it came on the radio, was *The Yellow Rose of Texas*." Vicky and Frank look at each other and smile.

I look over to Ginger, and she winks at me. She made sure yellow roses were everywhere—as sort of a surprise theme of the evening—in table centerpieces, twisted around the columns, and hanging in garlands with twinkling lights strung through the yard. Everything looks gorgeous.

"Now, we know you all are very successful, dignified people, but you live in Texas. And, like my parents, you were also falling in love and having babies in the sixties and seventies. Underneath those tuxedos and evening gowns, we know you are a bunch of hippie cowboys and cowgirls at heart."

Everyone laughs. Okay, this is going well. One older man with a black cowboy hat yells out, "Yee-haw!"

"That's right!" John grins at him. "We knew this. So we wanted to pay a tribute to our own Yellow Rose of Texas, my mother, Victoria Miller. Here's to you, mom and dad."

The back door opens and Vanessa walks out onto the patio, dressed in cowboy boots, jeans, and a white cotton tunic shirt. She's wearing a wreath of wildflowers on her gleaming blonde hair; her blue eyes are sparkling. She looks like a gorgeous seventies country singer. She pulls a stool up to the microphone and sits down with her guitar.

When I drove home from the sheep farm that day in April, I called Vanessa and asked if she'd meet us in Dallas to do this for us. She said she'd love to. College roommates are the best.

Vanessa addresses the expectant crowd. "We know Frank and Vicky have a tremendous love for each other and their families. Not only are they blessed with their two grown sons, but they also have five beautiful grandchildren. I'd like to introduce to you—Maddie, Drew, Daniel, Joy and Michael!"

Maddie carries Michael; Drew, Daniel and Joy follow her. They all walk to the front and stand next to Vanessa's stool and the microphone. Vanessa starts to play the guitar and sing *The Yellow Rose of Texas*.

*Please don't pick your noses, I'm silently begging the kids.*

When Vanessa gets to the chorus, the kids join in:

> *She's the sweetest little rosebud that Texas ever knew,*
> *Her eyes are bright as diamonds, they sparkle like the dew;*

They all sing beautifully and even little Joy remembers all the words. (Michael's job is to look cute.)

As they sing the chorus for the last time, each child plucks a tissue-wrapped long-stemmed yellow rose from a hidden vase and presents it to Vicky.

> *You may talk about your Clementine, and sing of Rosalee,*
> *But the yellow rose of Texas is the only girl for me.*

They each give Vicky a kiss and hug, while she wipes tears from her eyes. Frank beams and gives them each a hug. I notice Aunt Anne sniffling and dabbing at her eyes with her napkin.

The children bow and curtsey as the crowd erupts in cheers. Then, one by one, everyone rises and gives a standing ovation! I look at John and grin. Vanessa beams at me and I give her a thumbs-up.

The children scurry off into the house where a babysitter waits, and Vanessa starts playing again; this time she plays *Luckenbach, Texas*. Her clear, honest voice floats through the night air. Frank takes Vicky's hand and leads her to the patio and they start two-stepping to the music.

The man in the black hat yells again, "Yee-haw!" and grabs his wife's hand. Soon other couples are pairing off, white haired men and women dancing on the patio, the stone walkway, even kicking off their shoes and dancing in the grass. Whew! Everyone is loving this. I can breathe now.

John comes over to our table and asks me, "May I have this dance?" How is this man my husband? He's entirely too polished and handsome for me.

"Absolutely." I take his hand. John and I dance on the grass under the glittering crystals of the chandelier.

"Good speech, babe," I whisper to him.

"Hey, it was your idea," John says back.

He kisses me on the lips as Vanessa's voice sings about Luckenbach, Texas and "getting back to the basics of love."

*****

Vanessa has totally wowed this crowd. She has sung a mix of folk, country, bluegrass, and gospel. She sang *This Land is Your Land*, *If I had a Hammer*, and *Amazing Grace*. Everyone seems to adore her.

I heard a woman say to her friend, "I want to book her for Tim's birthday party! She's just what I've been looking for!"

Ginger glides up to congratulate me, "Good job, Julianne. You saved the day. I was beginning to panic about finding entertainment. Vanessa's perfect! Everyone thinks she's famous!

People are asking me, 'Where did you *find* her?' Can I give out her name and number? People are asking about a CD."

"Wow, I don't know." I don't think Vanessa even has business cards. "I'll ask her. Why don't you get their cards and she can email people when she gets home."

"Great idea." Ginger hurries off.

I sit down at one of the tables. My feet hurt, even though I kicked off those heels long ago. I sit and look up at the stars twinkling through the tree branches. They look like tiny jewels, hung out on the black velvet sky just for the occasion.

I am so thankful Frank and Vicky liked the kids' serenade. As I thought about what to get them, I realized it should include their families. I realized they were truly, as Louisa May Alcott says in Little Women, "rich in the blessings which alone can make life happy."

I realized Frank and Vicky value what everyone values when you get right down to it: the invisible. We all value the things that are unseen; sometimes we just forget. We think we value ease and luxury, diamonds and crystal, but we don't. We value fulfilling work, truth and honor, family and friends, lives well lived, love freely given. Frank and Vicky and all their millionaire friends know what we all do when we think about it—what is seen is temporary, but what is unseen is eternal.

I listen to Vanessa's sweet voice sing *O, Master Let Me Walk with Thee.*

> *Teach me Thy patience; still with Thee*
> *In closer, dearer, company,*
> *In work that keeps faith sweet and strong,*
> *In trust that triumphs over wrong.*

Through the patio's French doors I can see the kids on the couch inside the house. Joy is cuddled up with Michael, and they are both asleep. Their dear, plump cheeks are flushed. I have to go kiss them.

I go inside, kiss the sleeping little ones, and sit down on the couch by Daniel. The babysitter takes Maddie and Drew upstairs to bed, and I put my arm around Daniel.

"Are you tired, buddy?" I ask him gently.

"Yeah, Mom. I'm so tired." I look at my watch. Yikes. It's eleven-thirty.

"Wow, you didn't complain at all. You've been in here playing so nicely with the babysitter. Thanks, Daniel. Let me go find Daddy and we'll go, okay?"

"Okay," he says. "Hey, Mom?" He holds up a glass root-beer bottle. "Can you put this in the recycling bin for me? If we can find it..." He looks around.

"Sure," I say. That sweet little boy, looking for the recycling bin.

"Actually, wait," Daniel says, in a voice that sounds too low to be his. "It's my responsibility. I'll take care of it. I'll do that while you go get Dad."

"Wow, thanks Daniel. That is so responsible of you. Thank you!" My heart is breaking. He's so grown up.

I think back to what he said when the children were practicing the song for tonight. I had been saying, "I hope everyone likes it."

And Daniel said, "We're not doing it for them."

"Who are we doing it for?" I asked, thinking he'd say Frank and Vicky.

"We're doing it for the Lord," he replied with certainty, like why would I ask such a strange question.

"You're a wise little man," I told him. "Where'd you learn that?"

"From you, Mom," he said simply.

Oh. Really? Oh.

Being a mother is so surprising. And humbling.

I go out on the patio blinking back tears from my eyes. I run into my Mom and Dad.

"What's wrong, honey?" My mom can always tell when I'm about to lose it.

"Oh, nothing. Daniel is just all grown up." I feel the tears stinging my eyes.

"Yeah, soon he'll be getting married," my dad says, smiling at me.

"Dad!" I moan, "Don't say that!"

"It's true," he says gently, pointing to Joy asleep on the couch. "That was just you yesterday, honey."

Oh, my lands. I start bawling. He gives me a hug.

"You're doing a good job, sweetheart. They're wonderful children," my mom says, giving me a hug and wiping away my tears.

"Praise the Lord," I whisper for the second time that night. What else could I say? I can't take credit for this.

"Cherish those children," my dad says, and I think even his eyes look a little misty. "They grow up fast."

"Okay," I choke out. Why do my parents always do this to me? "I better go find John."

"We'll see you tomorrow. I think Holly and Jay already left." My mom gives me one last squeeze, and I go find John. John walks inside to pick up Michael while I say goodbye to his family and thank Ginger and Dave for the party.

I carry Joy; John carries Michael and holds Daniel's hand and we all head out. I look at Michael's sleeping face in profile against John's shoulder: a crescent fringe of dark lashes sweeping out over his round cheek, the bump of his nose, his full rosy lips parted in sleep, and his tiny chin. He is all soft curves and tender beauty and peace.

I think of my dad's words. Children do grow up fast. I can't believe Michael is almost two. Daniel will be in second grade next year, and Joy will be in kindergarten. Kindergarten!

This year of homeschooling and mothering has been one of the hardest years ever, but one of the best. I wouldn't trade those hours with my children for all the treasure or leisure in the world. Soon my children will be grown, but I will always have those memories of Bible stories on the couch, collecting scarlet maple leaves, and laughing in the sun. Those memories are what I will remember, not the hard times. (Well, maybe I'll remember the hard times a little, but they were worth it.)

Our family walks around the side of the house, under an archway covered in garlands of lavender and yellow roses.

Funny thing about roses—once you've seen the beauty of the blooms, you barely remember the thorns.

As we wait for the valet to get our car, I hear Vanessa's voice singing one of our favorites.

"Family Song?" Daniel asks, looking up at John. His little voice joins mine and John's as we softly sing into the fragrant night:

> *Be Thou my Vision, O Lord of my heart;*
> *Naught be all else to me, save that Thou art.*
> *Thou my best Thought, by day or by night,*
> *Waking or sleeping, Thy presence my light.*
>
> *Riches I heed not, nor man's empty praise,*
> *Thou mine Inheritance, now and always:*
> *Thou and Thou only, first in my heart,*
> *High King of Heaven, my Treasure Thou art.*

# Appendix

## Homeschool Group Study Guide

## Homeschooling Resources

(books, CDs, websites, etc.)

# Homeschool Group Study Guide

## CHAPTER 1 – MAY

1. At the convention, Julianne was confronted with several people's approaches toward homeschooling, and each was convinced that their way was the best. Have you experienced that? How did you arrive at your current homeschool approach and why is it a good fit for your family?

2. When Lisa prayed for Julianne, she prayed that God would lead Julianne even though Julianne didn't know where she was going. Look up Hebrews 11:8. What are some other examples from the Bible when people followed God even though they didn't know what would happen?

3. Do you get overwhelmed and start feeling discouraged when you go to homeschool conventions? Why or why not? What are some reasons you like to go (if you do)?

4. What are you afraid about in your life right now?

5. Pray with the mom next to you for God's courage to walk in faith and follow where He leads you, even when it's scary.

## CHAPTER 2 – JUNE

1. At the birthday party, did you think Vicky (Julianne's mother-in-law) was trying to be critical or do you think Julianne was being oversensitive?

2. After the birthday party where Julianne felt criticized by her mother-in-law, Julianne's mother reminded her of Galatians 1:10. What does that verse say? What is something in your life that you've done because you are serving the Lord, even if other people think it's nuts?

3. Is your extended family supportive of homeschooling? If not, how do you handle it?

4. Pray with the mom next to you that you would both serve the Lord and not others.

**Optional Memory Verse: Galatians 1:10**
(This is NASB, but use whatever version you want. If you don't have a verse memory system, try using spiral-bound index cards, one card for each verse.)

*For am I now seeking the favor of men, or of God? Or am I striving to please men? If I were still trying to please men, I would not be a bond-servant of Christ. – Galatians 1:10*


## CHAPTER 3 – JULY

1. In this chapter, Joy had her Salvation Army meltdown. What did Julianne learn from that? What was your Most Embarrassing Mothering Moment Ever? What did you learn from it (other than to pray *that* didn't happen again)?

2. After the meltown, Julianne thinks, "talk about pride going before a fall." Look up Proverbs 16:18 and Micah 6:8. Have there been any parenting moments where pride went before a fall in your life?

3. Julianne's friend Vanessa helps her with getting organized. Is this an area you are good at (neatness/organization) or are your strengths in different areas? What is one thing God has helped you with in this area? (Don't focus on what you're not doing.)

4. Pray with the person next to you that God would reveal areas of pride in your life, and ask for His help with those. Pray for a humble heart that leans on Him.

## CHAPTER 4 – AUGUST

1. In California, at a Chick-fil-A, Julianne presses Daniel to finish his journal page, even though it is a struggle. Do you think that was the right thing to do? Then, she thinks about not doing any more for the trip, because he might not be ready yet. How do you know if your child is not developmentally ready for something or if he is just being lazy? How do you handle it if he isn't ready yet?

2. As they sit on the beach, Julianne thinks, "If I teach my children nothing else, I want to teach them to recognize true treasures – not jewels or palatial mansions, but this amazing world God created, the precious people around us, and His eternal Truth. For where my children's treasures are, there their hearts will also be." Look up Matthew 6:20-21. What do you want your children to treasure?

3. What is something your children treasure right now? What seems to be on their hearts and minds most often?

4. Take a moment and pray with the person next to you for each of your children to treasure God above the other distractions in their lives.

Optional: With your homeschool group, sing How Great Thou Art (sing without music unless you happen to have a piano and a piano player in the room.) The words are at the end of the August chapter.


## CHAPTER 5 – SEPTEMBER

1. Why does Julianne feel so discouraged after her first few days of school? What are some of the things that are hard for you about homeschooling?

2. Why do you think Julianne felt like she had to include so many things on her schedule?

3. Pair up with a mom older/younger than you. If you are the less experienced mom, ask the more experienced mom any questions you have about your schedule. See if she has any ideas for you. If you are the more experienced mom, share a typical day's schedule with the younger mom (now or when you had kids her age), *especially any things you have cut out because they weren't priorities for your family.*

4. Pray with the mom you just paired up with for God's wisdom as you find a routine that works well for your family and ages of your children. (The next time you see your prayer partner, ask her how it's going.)

## CHAPTER 6 – OCTOBER

1. At the homeschool co-op, Julianne vents to her friends about how hard homeschooling is for her. Do you have friends you call when you're having a bad day (or year)? What can we do or say to encourage each other? How might our responses unintentionally discourage someone in need of encouragement in the homeschool journey?

2. Julianne tells her friends that she looks around at all the other moms and they seem like they can do everything. She wonders what is wrong with her. Have you ever found yourself believing this lie? What is the truth?

3. The co-op moms talk about how their husbands often get what is left over at the end of the day. What is one way you can show your husband he's important too this week?

4. Is there anything you are doing to impress other people that might need to be cut out in order to have more time and energy for your husband?

5. Pray with the person next to you for God's wisdom to know what activities are most important, and which, if any, could be cut out.

**Optional Memory Verse: Matthew 6:20-21**
(This is NASB, but use whatever version you want. If you memorized the Gal. 1:10 verse, see if you can quote it to your prayer partner.)

*But store up for yourselves treasures in heaven, where neither moth nor rust destroys, and where thieves do not break in or steal; for where your treasure is, there your heart will be also.*
*– Matthew 6:20-21*


## CHAPTER 7 – NOVEMBER

1.  Julianne is very aware of her character flaws (she's messy, she has a weakness for McDonald's and Diet Coke, she yells at her kids). What are some of her strengths that she forgets about? What are some of your strengths as a mother (that you might forget about)?

2.  Julianne starts to compare her children's education with her sister-in-law's. Do you compare yourself against other schools or a relative's children? What are the things your children learn by being at home that those children don't?

3.  What are some ways you cultivate in your children an appreciation for God's beauty around them and His still, small voice? How have you seen technology (TV, computer, phones) affect your children? Look up I Kings 19:11-12. Do you think that verse applies here? If so, how?

4.  Tell the person next to you one strength you think she has as a mother. Pray with her and thank God for all the gifts He's given you both to mother your children.

## CHAPTER 8 – DECEMBER

1. After yelling at her kids, Julianne is humbled to tears on the kitchen floor and has to apologize to her children and ask their forgiveness. Why is this important?

2. Why did Julianne get angry? What was the root of it? Can you think of a situation in the last week where you responded in anger to your children? What is one way to respond differently the next time that situation happens?

3. Look up James 1:19-20. Also, 2 Timothy 2:24-25. Why is this so hard? How can we do this as moms—be slow to become angry? If God has helped you with anger in your life, share with the other moms some things you have learned.

4. At the YMCA, Julianne reads some verses on her verse memory cards. Do you memorize verses? How has God used them in your life? Look up Psalm 127:1 and Psalm 127:3. How have you seen that children are a gift from the Lord?

5. Take a moment to pray with the mom next to you to confess anger, pray for God's wisdom on how to be more gentle and patient with your children, and thank Him for the gift of them.

**Optional Memory Verse: Lamentations 3:22-23**
(This is NIV, but use whatever version you want. If you memorized the other verses, see if you can quote them to your prayer partner.)

*Because of the LORD's great love we are not consumed, for his compassions never fail. They are new every morning; great is your faithfulness. – Lamentations 3:22-23*

## CHAPTER 9 – JANUARY

1. In January, Julianne decides to keep homeschooling even though it's hard, because that's what she feels God is leading her to do. What is something you've done even though it was hard? Was it worth it?

2. How would you describe Julianne and John's relationship? Do you think he was a support to her in homeschooling? Why or why not?

3. In the beginning, Julianne set out to prove her mother-in-law wrong about homeschooling. What is her motivation after spending some time praying about it?

4. Look up Isaiah 54:13. Discuss.

5. Pray with the mom next to you. Thank God for providing a husband who supports you in homeschooling and works so that you can stay home. Thank Him for your husband's job, or pray for him if he needs a job.

## CHAPTER 10 – FEBRUARY

1. Did you think the homeschool mothers in the book represented a diverse group? Why do you think the author chose to only include Christian mothers in the

homeschool co-op? Do you think the book reinforced stereotypes about homeschoolers or dispelled them?

2. Would you call Lisa, Julianne's mentor? Look up I Thessalonians 2:8 and Titus 2:3-5. How did Lisa apply those principles with Julianne?

3. Julianne mentions serving her friend Elizabeth and paraphrases Deuteronomy 6:6-9. Please look up those verses. What are some practical ways you teach your children to serve as you go about your life?

4. Pray with the mom next to you and thank Him for this group of moms you are with right now.

**Optional Memory Verse: Isaiah 54:13**
(This is NIV, but use whatever version you want. If you memorized the other verses, see if you can quote them to your prayer partner.)

*All your children will be taught by the LORD, and great will be their peace. — Isaiah 54:13*


## CHAPTER 11 – MARCH

1. School is getting easier for Julianne now. Why? What has changed since the beginning of the school year?

2. Julianne mentions one of the advantages of homeschooling is that her children get to spend time with their little brother. Do you think your children are closer to each other because you homeschool? What are the other advantages you've seen for your family?

3. Julianne mentions movement and hands-on activities being good for her son. Do you have children who struggle to sit still and pay attention? What are some ways you've helped them learn?

4. Please look up I Corinthians 3:6. Who brings the growth?

5. Thank God for bringing the growth in your children. Ask Him for their hearts to grow strong in His love.


## CHAPTER 12 – APRIL

1. At the sheep farm, Julianne and her friend Vanessa discuss their schooling decisions. Why have you chosen the schooling options you have? Have people criticized you for it? Do you feel you have to defend your decision to others?

2. Look up Isaiah 40:11. Discuss. How has God led you and your husband in your parenting?

3. What are some practical ways to show grace to other mothers, even if their parenting decisions are different from yours?

4. Thank God for leading you in your decisions. Pray that instead of looking around to see what other moms think, we would keep our eyes on the Shepherd, who is leading us.

**Optional Memory Verse: Isaiah 40:11**
(This is NASB, but use whatever version you want. If you memorized the other verses, see if you can quote them to your prayer partner.)

*He tends his flock like a shepherd: He gathers the lambs in his arms and carries them close to his heart; he gently leads those that have young. — Isaiah 40:11*


## CHAPTER 13 – MAY

1. What is Julianne's true gift to Frank and Vicky? How would you describe her feelings toward Vicky at the end of the book?

2. What was the symbolism of the yellow roses?

3. Discuss the role of the art, poetry, and hymns throughout the book. Which ones stood out to you and why? How did they parallel the story?

4. What do you think Julianne learned during the year? What did you take away from the book?

5. With the mom next to you, thank God that He has given you the gifts to teach your children. Pray that He would help you apply whatever you learned from this book and be an encouragement to another mom. (If you memorized the verses in this study, try to quote them to your prayer partner. )

   **Optional:** With your homeschool group, sing Be Thou My Vision (without music unless you happen to have a piano and a piano player in the room).

*Be Thou my Vision, O Lord of my heart;*
*Naught be all else to me, save that Thou art.*
*Thou my best Thought, by day or by night,*
*Waking or sleeping, Thy presence my light.*

*Riches I heed not, nor man's empty praise,*
*Thou mine Inheritance, now and always:*
*Thou and Thou only, first in my heart,*
*High King of Heaven, my Treasure Thou art.*

# Homeschooling Resources

*This is a work of fiction. However, I wanted it to be a resource for homeschoolers and potential homeschoolers. The fictional items from the book are listed first; followed by real resources for homeschooling and life.*

**Fictional**

- Classical Advantage, Exploring God's Creation, and A Natural Education are fictional programs
- Dalton Prep and Redbud Christian Academy are fictional schools.
- *Superfood Mommy* is a fictional blog.

## CHAPTER 1 – MAY

### BOOKS

- Welchel, Lisa: *So You're Thinking About Homeschooling* (an excellent overview of the different approaches to homeschooling.)
- Wilson, Todd: *Help! I'm Married to a Homeschooling Mom!* (and Todd's book *Lies Homeschooling Moms Believe* is a great one for moms.)

### OTHER RESOURCES

**Different Homeschool Approaches** – Many homeschoolers use a mix of ideas and materials from different methods. (You don't have to figure out what 'approach' you want to use before you start. Your theories may change once you try something.)

- Classical - *The Well Trained Mind* is a good introduction to the Classical method of homeschooling. For a classical memory program, please visit www.classicalconversations.com.

- Charlotte Mason - www.amblesideonline.org. *A Charlotte Mason Companion* by Karen Andreola is a good introductory book. Another website is www.simplycharlottemason.com .

- Literature-based – Sonlight (www.sonlight.com), Tapestry of Grace (www.tapestryofgrace.com)

- Unschooling– http://www.holtgws.com/whatisunschoolin.html

- Unit Studies – www.konos.com

- Hands-On, mix of Charlotte Mason and Classical – My Father's World (www.mfwbooks.com )

- Traditional – some of the larger companies include: A Beka (www.abeka.com), Bob Jones (www.bjupress.com), Rod and Staff (www.rodandstaffbooks.com), and Saxon (saxonhomeschool.hmhco.com).

- There are many other educational approaches including Reggio Emilia, Waldorf, and Montessori that can be adapted to homeschooling. With any approach, use discernment and wisdom to decide which aspects are best for your family.

- Many of these resources are Christian-based resources. If you want secular resources, the book *The Well-Trained Mind* has many suggestions. Saxon is a well-respected secular program.

**Other products, available at amazon.com or teacher supply stores**

- Handwriting Without Tears – multi-sensory handwriting program for pre-K and up
- Laurie Toys – hands on for toddlers
- Apologia science books
- Butterfly houses, ant farms
- Counting bears
- Melissa & Doug puzzles
- Math Manipulatives: Unifix cubes, pattern blocks, Cuisenaire Rods (dried beans, toothpicks, Cheerios, and buttons work well too)

**General Websites**

- www.thePioneerWoman.com/homeschooling - blog by Ree Drummond, homeschooling section by Heather Sanders and Kristen Chase. Good online community.

- www.aholyexperience.com – encouragement for moms, written by Ann Voskamp, author of One Thousand Gifts and homeschooling mom, about giving thanks for the ordinary.

- www.owlhaven.net – written by Mary Ostyn, a homeschooling mom of ten, with information on living on a budget, homeschooling, and other practical topics.

- www.wholeheart.org – written by Sally Clarkson, author and speaker on motherhood and home education.

- www.lisawhelchel.com – Lisa Whelchel's site. The homeschooling tab has links to lots of online resources for those just getting started.

- www.Familymanweb.com – Todd Wilson's encouragement for dads and homeschooling moms.

# CHAPTER 2 – JUNE

## BOOKS

### Board Books

- Boynton, Sandra: *Moo, Baa, La La La*
- Brown, Margaret Wise: *The Big Red Barn*
- Fox, Mem: *Where is the Green Sheep?*

# CHAPTER 3 – JULY

### None

# CHAPTER 4 – AUGUST

## BOOKS

### Easy Reader Books

- McNulty, Faith: *Listening to Whales Sing*
- Turner, Ann and Barrett, Robert: *Dust for Dinner*

### Picture Books

- Bishop, Jennie: *The Princess and the Kiss (a purity story for girls)*

## OTHER RESOURCES

### Websites for Educational Opportunities in Orange County, California

- The Ocean Institute    www.ocean-institute.org
- San Juan Capistrano Mission www.missionsjc.com
- Pretend City Children's Museum www.pretendcity.org

# CHAPTER 5 – SEPTEMBER

## BOOKS

### Chapter Books

- Atwater, Florence and Richard: *Mr. Popper's Penguins*
- Dahl, Roald: *Charlie and the Chocolate Factory*
- Estes, Esther: *The Hundred Dresses*
- Lindgren, Astrid: *Pippi Longstocking*
- Miller, Susan Martens: *Hudson Taylor (and all Chronicles of Faith series)*
- Wilder, Laura Ingalls: *Little House series, all*

### Picture Books

- Cheney, Lynn: *America; A is for Abigail; Our 50 States*
- De Paola, Tomie: *Favorite Nursery Tales* (illustrated by de Paola)
- Hunkin, Oliver: *A Dangerous Journey: Pilgrim's Progress for Children*
- Stevenson, Robert Louis: *A Child's Garden of Verses* (There are many versions. Two good ones are published by DK (with fine art to accompany the poems) and Chronicle Books (beautiful illustrations).)

### Easy Reader Books

- Rylant, Cynthia: *Henry and Mudge books; Mr. Potter and Tabby books; all others*
- Parish, Peggy: *Amelia Bedelia books*
- Selsem, Millicent: *Greg's Microscope*
- Roop, Peter and Connie: *Keep the Lights Burning, Abbie*
- McLerran, Alice: *Roxaboxen*

**Beginning Reading (equivalent to easiest level of Easy Reader books)**

- Maslen, Bobby Lynn: *Bob books*; published by Scholastic

- Seuss, Dr.: *The Cat in the Hat, others*

**Board and Lift-the-Flap books**

- No titles specified

## OTHER RESOURCES

**Curriculum**

- "Baby Bible" Program for Toddlers www.SeeandKnow.com

# CHAPTER 6 – OCTOBER

## BOOKS

- Glaser, Linda: *Emma's Poem* (about the Statue of Liberty)

# CHAPTER 7 – NOVEMBER

## BOOKS

- Alcott, Louisa May: *Little Women*

**Thanksgiving Books**

- Dagliesh, Alice: *The Thanksgiving Story*

- Devlin, Wende: *Cranberry Thanksgiving*

- Hines, Gary: *Thanksgiving in the White House*

- Spinelli, Eileen: *Thanksgiving at the Tappleton's*

- Waters, Kate: *Tapenum's Day: A Wompanoag Indian Boy in Pilgrim Times*

## OTHER RESOURCES

### Memory CDs

- States and Capitals CD  www.audiomemory.com

## CHAPTER 8 – DECEMBER

### Christmas Books (Listed on Weekly Lesson Plan)

- Bronson, Linda (illus.): *Sleigh Bells and Snowflakes*
- Busch, Melinda: *Born on Christmas Morn*
- Chaconas, Dori: *On a Wintry Morning*
- Forrester, Maureen: *Joy to the World*
- McKissack, Patricia: *The All-I'll-Ever-Want-for-Christmas Doll*
- Noble, Trinka Hakes: *Apple Tree Christmas*
- Ransome, James: *A Joyful Christmas*
- Riordan, James: *Favorite Stories of the Ballet (Nutcracker)*
- Spirin, Gennady (illus.): *Twelve Days of Christmas*
- Tews, Susan: *Gingerbread Doll*
- Wojciechowski, Susan: *The Christmas Miracle of Jonathan Toomey*

## OTHER RESOURCES

### Movies

- The Sound of Music
- Mary Poppins
- White Christmas

# CHAPTER 9 – JANUARY

## BOOKS

**Parenting Books (Discussing simplicity—less technology, less structured activities, more time in nature—for the emotional, intellectual and physical health of children.)**

- Elkind, David: *The Hurried Child*
- Healy, Jane: *Endangered Minds: Why Children Don't Think and What We Can Do About It*
- Louv, Richard: *Last Child in the Wood: Saving Our Children from Nature Deficit Disorder*
- Payne, Kim John: *Simplicity Parenting (though this is not written from a Christian worldview, many of the practical ideas on simplifying family life can be helpful)*
- Wilson, Todd: *Taming the Techno-Beast (Discusses relational and spiritual impact of too much technology.)*

## OTHER RESOURCES

### Chores/Organization

- www.titus2.com The book *Managers of Their Chores* has a book and supplies for a Chore System (it comes with Chore Packs™ and cards). The book *Managers of Their Homes* has information on creating a workable daily schedule. Also, their CDs on "Anger, Relationship Poison" and "Homeschooling with a Meek and Quiet Spirit" are excellent for dealing with anger (getting mad at our kids) and gentleness.

- Brenneman, Kim: *Large Family Logistics: The Art and Science of Managing the Large Family* – excellent ideas for families of all sizes (not just large ones)

# CHAPTER 10 – FEBRUARY

## BOOKS

### Winter Books

- Brett, Jan: *The Mitten; The Gingerbread Baby*
- Conley, Lucy: *The Lost Milk Jar* (rodandstaffbooks.com )
- dePaola, Tomie: *Pancakes for Breakfast*
- Frost, Robert. Illustrated by Susan Jeffers: *Stopping By Woods on a Snowy Evening*
- Keats, Ezra: *The Snowy Day*
- Neitzel, Shirley: *The Jacket I'll Wear in the Snow*
- Shulevitz, Uri: *Snow*

### Board Books

- Gerth, Melanie: *Ten Little Ladybugs; Good Night, Sweet Butterflies*

# CHAPTER 11 – MARCH

## BOOKS

### Civil War Books

- Brenner, Martha: *Abe Lincoln's Hat*
- D'Aulaire, Ingri and Edgar: *Abraham Lincoln*
- Fritz, Jean: *Just a Few Words, Mr. Lincoln*
- Gayle, Sharon: *Harriet Tubman and the Freedom Train*
- Hines, Gary: *Thanksgiving in the White House*
- Woodruff, Elvira: *Dear Austin (chapter book)*

### Project Books

- Broida, Marian: *Projects about Plantation Life* (Hands-On History)

- King, David: *Civil War Days* (American Kids in History)

**Books on CD**

- Any that your local library has that look good to you.

## OTHER RESOURCES

### Music

- McGill, Alice; *In the Hollow of Your Hand: Slave Lullabies*
- Mattox, Cheryl Warren; *Shake it to The One that You Love Best: Play Songs and Lullabies from Black Musical Traditions*
- Swing Low, Sweet Chariot (traditional hymn)
- Glory, Glory Hallelujah (traditional hymn)

### Movies

- Famous Americans for Children: Abraham Lincoln, Harriet Tubman
- An Apple for Harriet Tubman (also a book)
- Follow the Drinking Gourd (also a book)

## RECIPES

**Fruit (Green) Smoothie Recipe (Great for kids, babies and Mommies. Even Daddies!)**

- Juice (apple or orange)

- Frozen banana (peel overripe bananas and freeze in Ziploc bag in freezer). Adds sweetness.

- Frozen berries (strawberries or blueberries, blackberries, mango)

- Greens (raw spinach or kale, start with one handful, add more as you get used to it)

- Avocado (optional. Try without it first.)

Blend. Enjoy!

### Chocolate Banana Milkshake (with stealth greens)

- Milk (if milk allergies, can use soy, almond, coconut, rice milk, etc.)

- Frozen banana (peel overripe bananas and freeze in Ziploc bag in freezer). Adds sweetness.

- Cocoa powder (to taste)

- Greens (raw spinach or kale, start with one handful, add more as you get used to it)

- Optional: a little sugar or honey (with the sweet bananas, you probably won't need it)

Blend. Enjoy!

## CHAPTER 12 – APRIL

### OTHER RESOURCES

#### Websites

- **Homeschool CDs (for Moms & Dads):** This is an excellent way to learn while you are cleaning the kitchen or folding laundry. Google the homeschool convention in your state, then go to their website and order CDs from past conferences on topics that interest you. CDs are usually about $6.00 each. If you can't get to a convention, this is a wonderful way to get quality information right at home. You can also ask homeschooling moms if they have CDs from past conferences you could borrow.

- **Information (and CDs about) Teaching Highly Distractible Children-** www.sizzlebop.com Click on 'Carol's Web Corner' for practical free tips. Click on 'Sizzlebop Store' to order CDs. (I think her ideas are helpful for any child, especially boys!)

- Awana Bible memory program: www.awana.org

- Shepherd's Cross sheep farm: www.shepherdscross.com

- Homeschool laws by state: www.hslda.org/hs/state (Homeschool Legal Defense Association)

**Spring Activities**

- **Simple Messianic Passover Dinner**
  Wertheim, Janie-sue: *Walk with Y'shua Through the Jewish Year*

  *The above book has ideas for celebrating the traditional Jewish holidays with children, with a focus on Y'shua (Jesus). A Passover Seder can be as simple as paper plates with unleavened bread, horseradish, parsley, and charoset (apple mixture). Each person gets a cup with salt water (to dip parsley in) and grape juice to drink. Tell the kids the symbolism of each (look this up online) and read about the first Passover with Moses, and Jesus' Passover at the Last Supper in the Bible. You can read more online, but don't get intimidated. Start simply.*

- **Resurrection Rolls**
  Get some yeast freezer rolls, the kind that has to rise for 3-5 hours. Let them rise. When risen, your kids hide a big marshmallow in the center of each one, wrap the roll around, sprinkle with cinnamon and

sugar and put it on a cookie sheet. Bake normally.
When the rolls are done, the marshmallow is gone!
It symbolizes the empty tomb! These rolls are a
great, easy, fun activity and can be served with the
Easter meal or as dessert.

- **How to make a clover crown**

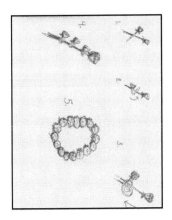

# CHAPTER 13 – MAY

## BOOKS/CURRICULA- Teaching Your Child to Read/Phonics

- A Beka Kindergarten Phonics book: *Letters and Sounds K*
- Use with the A Beka *Handbook for Reading*

### OR whichever one you like best of the following:

- Englemann, Siegfried, Haddox, Phyllis and Elaine Bruner; *Teach Your Child to Read in 100 Easy Lessons*
- Hiskes, Dolores; *Phonics Pathways*
- Wise, Jessie; *The Ordinary Parent's Guide to Teaching Reading*
- Any other reading/phonics program recommended to you

Julianne's homeschool journey still continues. Read more at:

**www.thehomeschoolexperiment.com**

*"Reminding dads and moms of what's most important"*

To obtain additional encouraging homeschool resources for moms and dads, visit:

**www.familymanweb.com**